Can you prov

Developing concepts of proof in primary and secondary schools

Sue Waring

The Mathematical Association

First published in 2000 by
The Mathematical Association
259 London Road
Leicester LE2 3BE
United Kingdom

ISBN 0 906588 44 8

Printed and bound in Great Britain at
J. W. Arrowsmith Ltd, Bristol.

Typeset by Bill Richardson

Preface

This book arose out of a thesis based on research undertaken by the author, as part-time student and full-time teacher, although its origins go back much further.

The focus of the research was directly affected by the conflict between memories of pleasurable experiences when learning proofs as a schoolgirl, and the realisation, as a teacher in the early 1980s, that pupils were no longer exposed to these experiences. Not everyone has the same positive memories of school mathematics in the 1950s. For many pupils rote learning of some proofs and difficulties in writing proofs in an unnatural (to pupils) style were detrimental to their learning of mathematics. However, the wisdom of removing almost all reference to proof for all pupils during the curriculum changes of the 1960s has recently begun to be questioned.

The creation of a curriculum based on the perceived needs of pupils "from the bottom up" instead of the "top down" approach influenced by the universities was laudable but had both negative and positive impact. In replacing Euclidean geometry with the more accessible transformation geometry the new curriculum removed almost all traces of proof. So it no longer presented mathematics as an example of a unified logical system. The absence of proof impoverishes the mathematical experience of all pupils. The fact that methods of teaching it to date have not been appropriate for many pupils is not a valid reason for its neglect. Shifting the emphasis from the study of deductive, mainly formal, proofs to other more informal proofs makes ideas of proof accessible to more, and younger, pupils.

Although the disappearance of proof was a gradual process, which took place mainly during the 1970s, its absence was very noticeable to the author soon after returning to the classroom after a nine year break. It was pleasing to see that pupils were no longer required to rote learn proofs but it was disconcerting to realise that the ability to prove was no longer tested in "O-Level" mathematics examinations. Questions about proving theorems in geometry were replaced by calculations of angles and lengths; and proofs in other aspects of the curriculum were not examined. The effect of this shift in emphasis was clearly demonstrated to the author by the puzzled expressions on the faces of a group of "A-Level" students at this time, when they were asked why the sum of the angles of a triangle was 180°. This reinforced her belief that proof is a vital component of mathematics and should be part of pupils' mathematical experience, even if not explicitly tested.

The changes incurred by the advent of GCSE (1988) and the National Curriculum (1991) did not improve the situation. Proof was still accorded a very low priority when the research was started. Early drafts of the book expressed the purpose of the book as "raising the profile of proof". It was gratifying to be able to change this to "show how the curriculum can be delivered" in the light of recent changes to the (English) National Curriculum, which dramatically raise the profile of proof for all pupils.

The research referred to above, which uses many of the proof activities in this book, provided evidence to support its hypotheses, namely:–

- experience in mathematical proof enhances appreciation of the need for proof;
- experience in mathematical proof improves ability to understand the nature of proof;
- experience in mathematical proof improves ability to construct a proof;
- teaching about proof through pattern is a viable alternative/ addition to teaching about proof by other methods.

This led the author to the conclusion that proof activities, especially those based on patterns, are a valuable feature of mathematics in primary and secondary schools. The first three hypotheses form the basis for the programme in the book, designed to teach proof in three phases:– "Learning about proof", "Learning to prove" and "Improving proof skills".

The prolonged neglect of explicit references to proof means that there are likely to be many younger teachers who have limited experience of proof in school mathematics; and many older teachers are more likely to have experience of learning and teaching only formal deductive proofs. The material and guidance in this book are intended to support both groups. In the first two phases, class discussions aim to develop explanations of new (to pupils) mathematics, and are generally accompanied by diagrams. The emphasis in proof activities is on proof as an explanation of the structure of pattern. The third phase uses a more formal approach to proof for older, able pupils.

The question "Can you prove it?", which forms the subtitle of this book, is implicit at all stages of learning and teaching about proof. Initially it is asked by the teacher of pupils in order to raise their awareness of the existence of proof. At an early stage pupils are encouraged to ask the teacher to prove new claims as they learn to expect that justification is almost always possible. In preparing to answer these questions teachers will need to be able to prove to themselves all the mathematics they teach to pupils. Finally, an important objective of teaching proof is that pupils begin to ask themselves such questions. The following diagram would seem to summarise the directions for this question:–

The author

I began teaching in a girls' grammar school in 1966. A career break of almost nine years (1969-77) to raise two daughters created opportunities to teach part-time in both the primary and tertiary sectors. Return to part-time teaching in secondary schools provided experience in girls', boys', and mixed selective and comprehensive schools. In 1991 I embarked on part-time study for an M.Ed. in Mathematical Education, followed by research for a doctoral thesis completed in 1997, both at the University of Leeds.

Acknowledgements

I wish to thank the following people for their assistance:–

my husband, Eric, for his moral support and practical help in many ways;

Anthony Orton and Tom Roper for their guidance during the preparation of my thesis;

Peter Bailey, Bill Richardson and others of the Mathematical Association, for helpful comments and support in preparing the manuscript for publication; and finally

the pupils I have taught, especially those at Queen Elizabeth's High School, Gainsborough, who participated in the research.

To Eleanor Kate.

CONTENTS

Chapter 3

Phase 2 – Teaching and learning to prove
"Convince a penfriend"

Chapter 4

Phase 3 – Improving proof skills
"Towards formal proof"

Chapter 5

Proof in sixth forms and colleges

"Proof for all"

Chapter 6
Implementing a proof-orientated curriculum
"Raising the profile of Proof"

Proof tables

The three pages following contain lists of proofs, the method involved, the Proof Level (PL) and the page. The Proof Levels are coded as

2b/3

Generic example and a generalised proof are both considered.

3/4 and 3/5 Differentiated by outcome:–

    3 – pupil understands proof

    4 – pupil can write own proof about this pattern

    5 – pupil can write this and other proofs in Phases 2 and 3.

    5+ indicates pupil can understand and write proof in a formal style.

Phase 1 proofs (in Chapter 2)   *"Convince a friend"*

Proof Discussion	*Proof/Reasoning Method*	*PL*	*Page*
Adding odd/even numbers	Picture/deduction	2b/3	28
Adding consecutive odd numbers	Picture	2b/3	30
Adding consecutive integers from 1	Deduction/picture	2b/3	31
Divisibility tests	Deduction/picture	2b	33
Commutativity of + and ×	Picture	2b	34
Area of rectangles	Generic examples	2b	34
Angles at a point	Definition/axiom	–	35
Angles on a straight line	Transformational/deduction	3	36
Right-angles	Definition/deduction	3	36
Vertically opposite angles	Transformational/deduction	3	36
Angles and parallel lines	Axiom/transformational/ deduction	3	37
Angles in a triangle	Demonstration/ transformational/deduction	3	38
Probability (one event)	Deduction	3	41
Probability (two events)	Exhaustion	3	42
Proof Activity			
Bricklaying	Induction/deduction	3	45
A rose hedge	Induction/deduction	3	48
Lollipop lines	Induction/deduction/ generic example	2b/3	50
Overlapping circles	Induction/deduction	3	55
Row of squares	Induction/deduction	3	60
Reverse and add	Generic examples	2b	63
Reverse and subtract	Generic examples	2b	68
Handshakes	Demonstration/induction/ picture/deduction	3	71
A new team strip	Exhaustion	3	77
Dot-to-dot triangles	Exhaustion	3	80
Row of triangles	Induction/deduction	3/4	86
"Not Proof"			
Multiplying directed numbers	Particular cases	2a	83
Recurring decimals	Empirical evidence	1	83
Adding "half"	Conjecture	0	84
True or false?	Paradoxes	–	84
Sharing camels	Paradox	–	85

Phase 2 proofs (in Chapter 3)   *"Convince a penfriend"*

Proof Discussion	Proof/Reasoning Method	PL	Page
Odd/even products	Picture/algebraic deduction	2b/3	89
Divisibility tests	Algebraic deduction	3	90
Multiplying binomials	Diagram/deduction	3	91
Areas (rectilinear shapes)	Deduction (dissection)	3	92
Circumference of circles	Definition/axiom	–	94
Area of circles	Deduction (dissection to infinity)	3	94
Volume of cuboids and prisms	Deduction (based on dissection)	3	95
Congruent triangles	Transformational reasoning	3	96
Angles in triangles	Deduction (Euclidean)	3	99
Angles in quadrilaterals	Deduction	3	100
Pythagoras' theorem	1. Perigal's dissection (demonstration)	0	101
	2. Particular case (3, 4, 5)	1	101
	3. Empirical evidence (measuring)	1/2	101
	4. Deduction (based on dissection)	3	102

Proof Activity

Angles in polygons	Induction/deduction	3/5	106
Staircase numbers	Deduction (dissection + algebraic)	3/4	115
Triangle numbers	Induction/deduction (picture + algebraic)	3/4	121
Crossing lines	Induction/deduction	3/4	127
Hydrocarbons	Induction/deduction	3/4	131
Spiked wall	Induction/deduction	3/4	135
Joined hexagons	Induction/deduction	3/4	138
L-shapes	Induction/deduction	3/4	141
Calendar squares	Deduction	3/4	145
Fenceposts	Induction/deduction	3/4	146
Product of consecutive integers	Deduction	3/4	149
Painted cubes	Induction/deduction	3/4	152
Frogs	Induction/deduction	3/4	153
Partitioning	Exhaustion	3/5	155
Windows	Induction/deduction	3/4	161

"Not Proof"

Regions in a circle	False deduction (empirical evidence)	1	157
Fallacies	Flawed proofs (algebra, number)	–	159
Square dissection	False conjecture	1	160

Phase 3 proofs (in Chapter 4)   *"Towards formal proof"*

Proof Discussion	Proof/Reasoning Method	PL	Page
Square roots	Counter-example	5	167
Fermat numbers/Primes	Counter-example/computer	5	167
Irrational numbers	Contradiction	5+	168
Binomial products	Deduction	5	169
Quadratic equations	Deduction	5	170
Sectors and segments	Deduction	5	170
Isosceles triangles	Deduction (Euclidean)	5	171
Angles in triangles	Comparison of proof methods	5+	171
Angles in circles	Diagram/deduction (Euclidean)	5+	173
Radius perpendicular to tangent	Contradiction	5+	175
Alternate Segment Theorem	Diagram/deduction (Euclidean)	5+	177
Pythagoras' Theorem 1	Deduction (equal areas)	5+	180
Pythagoras' Theorem 2	Deduction (similar triangles)	5+	181
Complementary angles	Deduction	5	182
Sine and Cosine Rules	Deduction	5	183
Proof Activity			
Angles in circles	Deduction	5+	184
Growing patterns	Induction/diagram/ algebraic deduction	5	190
Polyhedra/Euler's Theorem	Deduction/induction	5+	195
Rows of squares	Induction/deduction	5	199
Special arrangements	Exhaustion/counter example	5	200
Squares of squares	Induction/deduction	5	202
One less than square	Diagram/algebraic deduction	5	205
Reverse and Subtract	Algebraic deduction	5	207
"Not Proof"			
Volume of a pyramid	Empirical evidence	1	210
	Demonstration	2a	210
	"Approximate" proof	5+	211
0.9' = 1?	Empirical evidence + deductions	1/5	211
Zeno's 2nd paradox	Paradox (False deduction)	–	212
2 not prime	Paradox (False deduction using probability)	–	212

CHAPTER 1

Developing concepts of mathematical proof in school

This introductory chapter makes a strong case for developing ideas of proof in school mathematics. The development of pupil understanding of proof is described in six levels. A programme for teaching proof in three phases, from introducing the notion of proof to young children to enabling some older pupils to read and write more formal proof, provides –
"Proof-based mathematics for all pupils."

Introduction

Why teach proof?

"Proof is at the heart of mathematics" claims Anderson (1996, p 33). The author wholeheartedly supports this claim and, like some other mathematics educators, is concerned that in recent years proof has become almost extinct in school mathematics in England.

However significant changes proposed in the new version (July 1999) of the (English) National Curriculum for mathematics herald a welcome raising of the profile of proof in both primary and secondary schools. Indeed there is an explicit reference to pupils explaining their reasoning in the introduction to Key Stage 1 (p 37), and later a recommendation that in the "Shape, space and measures" component pupils should be taught to "use .... explanation skills as a foundation for geometrical reasoning and proof in later key stages." (p 39) This is a dramatic improvement on the 1994 proposals in which the first reference to developing skills of mathematical reasoning was in the introduction to Key Stages 3 and 4 and the only explicit reference to proof was as extension material.

The new version builds on the earlier introduction of ideas of proof by an expectation at Key Stage 2 that pupils should be taught to "develop logical thinking and mathematical reasoning" (p 42) in solving numerical problems; and to "use mathematical reasoning to explain features of shape and space" (p 43). At Key Stages 3 and 4 pupils are to be taught "to develop short chains of deductive reasoning and concepts of proof," (p 50) and "to distinguish between practical demonstration, proof, conventions, facts, definitions and derived properties" (p 53). Able pupils who progress to the Higher Level at Key Stage 4 are expected "to progress from the use of definitions and local chains of reasoning to the appreciation and explanation of how more complicated properties and results can be derived from simpler properties and results" (p 72).

The development of concepts of proof is well illustrated by the approach to teaching some geometry. After the initial reference to laying down foundations for proof at Key Stage 1, Key Stage 2 includes the expectation that pupils "know" that the sum of the angles in a triangle is 180° (p 59). This implies an awareness of this property arising from practical demonstration, like tearing off corners or measuring angles, but not necessarily an awareness of the notion of need for a generalised proof. This is not mentioned until Key Stage 3 when pupils are to be taught "to understand a proof ...." of this property (p 50). At the Higher Level of Key Stage 4 pupils are expected not only to know and use, but also to "establish", "explain" or "deduce", several angle and tangent properties of circles (p 70).

The purpose of this book is to show how this new curriculum, and other similar curricula, such as those in Northern Ireland and Scotland, can be delivered by informing teachers about proof opportunities in school mathematics, and offering support and guidance for incorporating proof into their teaching.

Until the 1960s pupils in British schools who were thought to be capable of studying mathematics were taught Euclidean geometry, including proofs of theorems. For many reasons, including the realisation that transfer of training to other areas of thinking was very limited, this was replaced by transformation geometry with little reference to proof. This state of affairs prevailed at the time of construction of the first version of the English National Curriculum in 1988 which aimed to cater for the needs of all pupils studying mathematics from five to sixteen years old. So it was not surprising that proof was only included for very able pupils who might attain the highest level (ten) at age sixteen.

Dowling was among those educators who regretted this and observed (Dowling and Noss, 1990, pp 45-46) that deduction was often absent from mathematics classrooms and that investigations were considered complete when a conjecture had been stated and tested empirically. Although the then current version of the National Curriculum included reference to pupils explaining their thinking, the emphasis was on knowledge of mathematical facts and procedures, and proof was accorded a low profile, exemplified by the fact that it rarely featured significantly in national tests. Perks and Prestage (1995, p 43) also expressed concern that "many texts and syllabuses pay scant attention to proof".

The author's experience in secondary school classrooms suggests that acceptance of an informal style of proof enables more pupils to understand the notion of proof, and to construct their own proofs, without the constraints of an unfamiliar language in the early learning stages. Awareness of the existence of a more formal style may be achieved by exposure to some Euclidean proofs, and proofs of mathematical facts in the curriculum. So, at the same time as learning to understand and create their own proofs, some pupils may also experience the language of formal mathematical proofs.

Many young adolescents are influenced by a currently prevalent perception of education that schools are the providers of knowledge which pupils must absorb in order to pass examinations. It is one rôle of professional educators to capitalise on the interests and ability of pupils to ask, and find answers to, questions by exposing them to situations which foster a more questioning attitude. Some mathematics educators acknowledge the contribution of proofs as examples of logical arguments; and the importance of providing pupils with opportunities to create their own proofs. For example, Anderson and Austin (1995, p 495), in an article concerning undergraduate understanding of proof, promote the notion of proof as "an inner conviction of certainty" and suggest that "the discipline of achieving this ..... is an intrinsic part of the study of mathematics".

The status accorded to proof in the curriculum has varied significantly during the history of mathematics teaching in schools. However, despite some lack of interest in teaching proof, there is general agreement amongst mathematics educators that problem-solving, which includes searching for patterns, plays an important rôle in teaching mathematics in school. While proof and problem solving are not exactly the same, they are very closely related. Indeed, Polya (1990, p 154) refers to "problems to prove" (e.g. Pythagoras' theorem) and "problems to find" (e.g. the number of squares, of all possible sizes, on a chessboard). A definition for mathematical problem solving (Threadgill-Sowder, 1985, p 332) is that it is "an activity which is goal directed and which involves a sequence of operations having a significant cognitive component, where the goal can be expressed in terms of mathematical content." Proving can be described, but not defined, in the same way and so could be considered as an example of problem solving.

An important contribution that proof makes to mathematics education is that it highlights interrelationships between areas of the mathematics curriculum. If new facts are proved to pupils rather than presented as new isolated items of knowledge, pupils may be led to appreciate mathematics as a unified whole rather than a series of discrete topics/facts. Examples of this are the use of algebra to establish properties of shapes and numbers, and analysis of shapes to establish algebraic relationships. If pupils are taught mathematics in this way they can be involved in a discipline in which any new statement can be justified by reference to previously proven truths. The act of proving forges links between concepts that have been mastered and new concepts, and enables pupils to be less dependent on memory for recall of separate facts. Jeffrey (1977, p 15) regrets the fact that many teachers lead pupils through a "relatively restricted number of skills" and exhorts them to "think of mathematics in terms of an act of mathematising rather than an accumulated body of mathematical knowledge because .... it will .... be a more realistic way of educating students to face an unknown mathematical future."

Pupils can thus begin to function as mathematicians and so become mathematically literate rather than just numerate. Teaching mathematics in this way might also have the advantage of fostering an approach to mathematics required by those embarking on degree courses in mathematics, and thus allay the concerns of some university teachers.

What is proof?

A definition of mathematical proof depends on the level of mathematics under consideration. For an expert mathematician proof may be a complex, rigorous, sometimes lengthy, argument. However for a learner of mathematics complexity, rigour and length are unlikely to be accessible and Porteous' definition (1994, p 5) that, "A proof of a statement is any adequate expression of the necessity of its truth" is more appropriate. Porteous states four criteria for the "adequacy" of a learner's proof, namely:

- "What is said must be true;
- .... a general statement requires a general treatment;
- .... the individual's description of why the statement is true must reflect an awareness of the logical necessity of that truth;

- the individual, having given the proof, must by that account consider the statement in question to be true."

Thus, in the context of learning mathematics complexity, rigour and length are not essential and a proof does not have to be formal in order to be valid.

Gardiner (1993), in an article critical of the low status accorded to proof in the current mathematics curriculum, argues that, provided mathematical reasoning is general and completely convincing, its form and language may depend on the "maturity and preparedness" of the learner. He makes a strong case for proof as an intrinsic component of school mathematics, believing that "reasons and reasoning are the mortar which binds the individual bricks of mathematics together". Slomson (1996, p 11), in an article expressing concern about what some teachers accept as proof, concedes that "the disadvantage of formal proofs is that they are often unintelligible". For him a good proof "not only convinces ..... but also helps us to understand".

Fischbein (1982, pp 10-18) states that "there are frequent situations in mathematics in which a formal conviction, derived from a formally certain proof is NOT (*sic*) associated with the .... feeling .... of real understanding", but also maintains that "fusion can always be attained". As examples he uses a diagram with minimal algebra to prove and explain the equality of vertically opposite angles; and "a story about lines and angles which can catch the spirit" of a more usual mathematical proof that angles of a triangle are supplementary. The story refers to "creating a triangle" by "inclining lines" so that one angle "accumulates what is lost" by another (p 39, method e).

Pope (1996, p 23) strongly advocates the use of diagrams as proofs, claiming that many pupils "grasp the image", rather than the alternative algebraic or geometric proof, more readily. Nelsen, (1995), gives examples of "proofs without words" and claims that "for a professional mathematician a good diagram can be proof enough". He includes the following proof that the addition of two consecutive triangle numbers is always a square number.

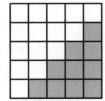

A proof without words

Martin and Harel (1989, p 42) assert that "the viewpoint that a mathematical proof must be a deductive argument is certainly held by mathematically sophisticated persons" and suggest that "persons with limited experience in mathematics often hold the view that an inductive argument can also be a mathematical proof". However Anderson and Austin (1995, pp 489-495) who, as university mathematics lecturers, can fairly claim to be "mathematically sophisticated", have no reservations about presenting inductive proofs to students as formal mathematical proof; and Tahta (1996, p 14) acknowledges that if he were forced to choose between teaching induction or deduction in schools he would opt for the former although he would much prefer to teach both.

Almost all proofs that have traditionally been included in the mathematics curriculum in secondary schools have been deductive. Such proofs satisfy a definition of deductive reasoning quoted by Simon (1996, p 198) as "referring to conclusions drawn from a logical chain of reasoning in which each step 'follows necessarily' (Ennis, 1969, p 7) from the previous". In the past this was often interpreted as requiring the use of formal mathematical language with some attempt at rigour. Simon (1996) also quotes a dictionary definition of inductive reasoning as "a generalised conclusion from particular instances" (Mish, 1991, p 615). This does not necessarily imply use of formal language and thus proof by induction in an informal style may be accepted, without loss of rigour, by pupils.

Proof by contradiction involves proving that the negation of the theorem leads to a contradiction and therefore cannot be true. This involves suspension of initial belief and thence the combination of two negatives to create a positive, which are both difficult concepts. If these are combined using only the formal language of mathematics the result is largely incomprehensible to most adolescents (and adults). Use of informal language such as "pretend" rather than "assume" may enable more pupils to understand such proofs in the initial construction, although use of formal language could be encouraged following understanding.

Polya describes such proofs as "indirect proofs" (1990, pp 215-221) and contrasts them with proof by "*reductio ad absurdum*" (1990, p 162) which involves showing "the falsity of an assumption by deriving from it a manifest absurdity". He also advocates the use of "incomplete proofs" in preference to presenting learners with unproven statements when a "complete proof" is too difficult for the learner. Although a strict logician would require a complete proof with "no gaps, no loopholes, no uncertainty" an incomplete proof is an acceptable alternative, in the context of teaching and learning proof, provided that it is not presented as complete to the learner, and that the teacher understands the complete proof.

Proof by counter-example may also be deemed appropriate for inclusion in a school curriculum. This entails proving that a proposed statement is untrue by discovering one example to the contrary. This type of proof has been neglected for school pupils, partly because of lack of suitable examples. However there are some patterns which appear to be predictable, but for which it is not difficult to find a counter-example, and which are therefore appropriate for use in the classroom. The activity "Regions in Circles" (p 157) provides such an example and is also discussed in a series of articles in "Mathematics in School" (Beevers, 1994; Gardiner, 1995b; and Anderson, 1995).

Proof by exhaustion involves testing all possible cases and is thus only practical in limited circumstances when the the number of cases is small. Because the possibility of examining all cases may be reassuring to pupils such proofs are appropriate in secondary schools. However care must be taken so that testing all cases is not confused with testing several particular cases in an infinite or large domain.

In discussing research on methods of proof Maher and Martino (1996, p 432) describe Balacheff's (1988) distinctions between justification, proof, and mathematical proof. Whereas justification is a discourse which aims to convince another individual of the validity of a statement, and proof is any explanation "accepted by a community at a given time", mathematicians would require a specifically mathematical proof. This book focuses on proof as an explanation of a pattern or property that is acceptable to mathematics educators who do not demand the rigour associated with formal mathematical proofs. However it also recognises the rôle of informal justification as a precursor to proof, and the importance of preparing some pupils for advanced studies in mathematics by exposing them to examples of more formal proofs.

Pupil understanding and perceptions of proof

Since pupils' ability to understand proof is dependent on their cognitive development, and in particular on their ability to reason logically and make deductions, it is considered helpful to refer to some of the most significant research in this domain.

Piaget's stage of "formal operational thought" was thought to be attained at about the age of twelve years, but Beard (1969, p 114) quotes experiments in Birmingham which suggest that a mental age of about thirteen is more common. During the previous stage of "concrete operational thought" reasoning is still in terms of objects and not hypotheses, and pupils in this stage can solve problems by inspecting concrete evidence and can only take into account a limited number of possibilities (McFarland, 1971, p 114). The transition from the "concrete" to the "formal" operational stage is gradual. Pupils slowly become more competent in dealing with implications and improve in their ability to "weigh the evidence" (Lovell, 1978, p 104). Beard (1969, p 98), in outlining this period, lists six new capacities which adolescents acquire as a result of seeing many points of view. They are:

  i)   acceptance of assumptions for the sake of argument;
  ii)   forming hypotheses which are expressed as propositions and then tested;
  iii) ability to generalise;
  iv)   appreciating the infinite;
  v)   awareness of thinking and ability to give logical justification for judgements;
  vi)   ability to deal with complex relations.

This hypothetical reasoning is independent of intrinsic truth or falsity and is a formal reasoning process.

To reflect the development of the concept of proof in pupils Balacheff (1988, pp 216-235) identifies four main types of proof: i) naive empiricism based on asserting the truth of a statement after verifying a few cases; ii) the crucial experiment designed so that the outcome determines the truth or falsity of an hypothesis; iii) the generic example showing truth or falsity based on results from a special case chosen as representative of a class and therefore involving decontextualisation; and iv) the thought experiment which is more general and abstract in that it is detached from a particular special case.

Bell (1976), after an analysis of responses of pupils aged 11-17 years to tasks that could involve proof, used a similar categorisation except that he also considered the "pre-proof" Stages 0 and 1, relating to understanding of pattern, before any development of understanding of proof. The subdivisions of Stage 2; namely 2.1, in which a few cases are checked unsystematically, and 2.2. involving more varied and systematic checking; broadly mirror the naive empiricism and crucial experiment of Balacheff. The remaining two stages are Stages 3 and 4. At Stage 3 pupils show an awareness of the need to deal with all cases, although this may be achieved through a generic example; and at Stage 4 they appreciate abstract proofs and demonstrate awareness of an axiomatic basis of the arguments, although they may still make mistakes due to failure to detect circularity in arguments.

Fischbein (1982, pp 9-18) asserts that "every teacher knows that a pupil is not a passive receiver of ..... solving procedures" and takes the view that "the intuitive structures are essential components of every form of active understanding and productive thinking". He identifies "three kinds of conviction" in the context of believing mathematical statements, namely: the formal type "imposed by a formal ...... argumentation", "the empirical inductive form .... derived from ..... findings which support the respective conclusion"; and the intuitive type "directly imposed by the structure of the situation itself", using the term "cognitive belief" to express this. He emphasises that "insightful understanding ..... is possible and necessary at each level of mathematical thinking".

Fischbein's "intuitive conviction" is similar to the "transformational reasoning" suggested by Simon (1996, pp 197-210). As an example of this Simon quotes a fifteen year old girl who explained that "if one base angle of an isosceles triangle were smaller, then the side enclosing it with the base would be longer" as proof that the base angles were equal. A second example demonstrates the rigidity of a triangle by visualising two moving line segments joined at one end (to be thought of as hinged wooden strips) fixed in position by a third segment of fixed length. If this segment is replaced by two or more hinged segments the structure is no longer rigid. He claims that transformational reasoning provides a sense of understanding the uniqueness of a triangle as a rigid figure among convex polygons, and illustrates that "a sense of understanding how it works" is a consequence of such reasoning.

The perceptions of proof in learners have been investigated by several researchers. Fischbein describes research into the awareness of high school pupils of "the profound distinction between empirical and formal .. proof" and found that only 14.5% perceived that the formal proof precluded the need for further empirical checks. He concludes that "in order to really understand what a mathematical proof means the learner's mind must undergo a fundamental modification". Vinner (1983, p 294) used a questionnaire in which academic high school students were asked to select preferred explanations for the fact that whole numbers of the form $n^3 - n$ are divisible by six because they can be shown to be the product of three consecutive integers, and concluded that at least one third of the sample did not understand the nature of proof. Bell *et al* (1983, pp 215-222) summarise earlier research including that of Williams (1978) and Robinson (1964), whose results were similar except that Robinson claimed that twelve-year-olds appreciated that checking is not equivalent to proving. Bell suggests that the difference may be accounted for by the possibility that this point might be sensitive to direct teaching. Bell *et al* (1983, p 221) also claim that pupils' use of a particular case as if it were general is widespread.

The research summarised above illustrates the fact that understanding and using mathematical proof involve complex mental processes and justifies the likelihood that pupils of primary and secondary school age will find aspects of proof difficult. The teacher's rôle is to provide an environment which fosters the development of logical reasoning in pupils and raises their levels of understanding of concepts of proof. In this book pupils' development of concepts of proof is described at six levels. These were originally proposed in a thesis, "The Teaching and Learning of Proof and Pattern in the Age Range Fourteen to Sixteen" (Waring, 1997), and are based on pupils' reactions observed during the research combined with the suggestions of Balacheff, Bell, and Fischbein.

Proof Levels

The following framework describes the development of proof concepts beginning with an appreciation of the need for proof, then an understanding of the nature of proof, and finally pupils' competence in constructing proofs. Thus the framework begins at **Proof Level 0**, which applies to pupils who have no appreciation of the notion of proof, and continues through five more levels to include pupils who understand the generalised nature of proof and its rôle in justifying conjectures, and who are also able to construct proofs in a variety of contexts.

Pupils who use "naive empiricism" (Balacheff, 1988) are at **Proof Level 1.** They recognise the existence of proof but do not appreciate its generalised nature. **Proof Level 2** represents a transitional stage between these two. Some pupils at this stage replace the few particular cases checked at Proof Level 1 with a greater number of particular cases, which are either more varied, eg. use larger numbers, or are randomly selected; others use a generic example to represent a class (Balacheff, 1988). Pupils who appreciate the generalised nature of proof are at **Proof Level 3.** They can follow a short chain of deductive reasoning but are not necessarily able to construct proofs. They can, however, distinguish between proof and practical demonstration. At **Proof Level 4** pupils can construct proofs in a limited range of contexts, including those which are familiar, and/or those which give rise to thought processes like "intuitive conviction" (Fischbein, 1982) or "transformational reasoning" (Simon, 1996), which a pupil may be able to express informally. Pupils at **Proof Level 5** have a deeper understanding of the nature and rôle of proof, and can construct proofs in a variety of contexts, possibly using some degree of formal language, where appropriate. All six levels, including a sub-division of Proof Level 2, are outlined below.

Proof Level 0: Pupils are ignorant of the necessity for, or even existence of, proof;

Proof Level 1: Pupils are aware of the notion of proof but consider that checking a few special cases is sufficient as proof;

Proof Level 2: Pupils are aware that checking a few cases is not tantamount to proof but are satisfied that either

a) checking for more varied and/or randomly selected examples is proof;

or b) using a generic example forms a proof for a class;

Proof Level 3: Pupils are aware of the need for a generalised proof and, although unable to construct a valid proof unaided, are likely to be able to understand the creation of a proof at an appropriate level of difficulty;

Proof Level 4: Pupils are aware of the need for, and can understand the creation of, generalised proofs and are also able to construct such proofs in a limited number of, probably familiar, contexts;

Proof Level 5: Pupils are aware of the need for a generalised proof, can understand the creation of some formal proofs, and are able to construct proofs in a variety of contexts, including some unfamiliar.

Although the standard attained by a pupil may be age-related inasmuch as ability to prove depends on cognitive development which is also age-related, this is not necessarily the whole story as both of these are likely to be influenced by pupil experiences. For example Jones (1994) provides evidence of primary school pupils who, when exposed to proof, demonstrate some ability to reason in mathematics. Perks and Prestage (1995) quote a seven-year-old pupil who produced a proof "with pictures", and Semadeni (1984) suggests that younger pupils can understand "action" proofs. Conversely personal research, described later in this book (see Chapter 4) provides evidence of fifteen-year-old pupils with no experience in proof being unable to prove, due to ignorance of the existence of proof and/or lack of understanding of its nature.

Teaching proof

Although there is a general consensus that proof in some form should be taught, and an implicit assumption that this will happen in the secondary schools, there are varying views as to exactly when teaching should begin. Brown (1995, p 36) advocates its inclusion from the beginning of secondary school because she believes that being "able to construct a mathematical model which allows the generation of an hypothesis which itself has to be proved true seems to be at the root of good method." The new English National Curriculum clearly takes the same view and introduces an informal approach to proof at Key Stage 1.

The fact that there is evidence to suggest that pupils in primary schools are capable of reasoning in the domain of pattern indicates that this might provide an appropriate source of proof activities. Patterns, since they involve repetition, are either visual or are composed of discrete quantities which can be represented by concrete apparatus or diagrammatically, and thus may be easier for pupils to prove. Explaining patterns does not necessarily involve use of mathematical language. Separating these two in the early stages of learning to prove might prevent pupils developing the attitudes of some university students who were unable to prove a number property because they expected the proof to require use of algebra (Perks and Prestage, 1995, pp 43-44). Providing pupils with experience in proof unclouded by mathematical language, effects the separation of these, and may make proof accessible to more pupils. It would therefore seem reasonable to suppose that pattern might be an appropriate domain for teaching proof.

Many of the proof activities suggested in this book are based on explaining patterns. In most of these the structure of visual patterns is explored, and the resulting number patterns related to the original structure. Other patterns arise out of investigating number properties such as divisibility tests or relationships between numbers such as differences between squares of consecutive integers. Additionally, some geometry properties are discovered through a search for patterns, which are then analysed and explained in relation to the original property.

Other geometric properties are explained, first informally and later in a more formal style; but it must be realised that not all pupils will be able to understand the latter. As pupils are introduced to algebra and some algebraic relationships and formulae, these too are proved at an appropriate level wherever possible. It is important to attempt to give reasons for all new mathematics taught to pupils and if this is not considered possible the lack of a generalised proof should be admitted and a demonstration of truth for a particular case, or group of cases, offered instead. The difference between the two should always be carefully explained. It may, however, be considered preferable to defer teaching some topics until pupils are able to understand at least an informal explanation.

Although using the domain of pattern for teaching proof in the early stages avoids some of the technical language associated with proof, this should not necessarily totally preclude the use of such language in the classroom. Indeed, it is important for teachers to increase pupils' mathematical vocabulary by using terms like "theorem", "converse", "corollary", and "implication". They should also use the names of proof methods like "deduction", "counter-example" and "contradiction" with older pupils and ensure that they can distinguish between proof and "not proof". This latter category includes axioms, conventions, definitions, and facts, and also practical demonstrations, empirical evidence, paradoxes and fallacies.

Background to the teaching programme

Many of the activities described here were included in a teaching programme designed as part of the research study to discover whether or not pupils in the age range fourteen to sixteen years could learn to prove, and whether or not using the domain of pattern for this enhanced their learning. This latter aspect is also discussed in Proof and Pattern" (Waring, Orton and Roper, 1999) in "Pattern in the Teaching and Learning of Mathematics" (Orton (Ed.), 1999).

The twenty-five pupils who formed the experimental group were in Year 10 (aged fourteen and fifteen years), and between the tenth and twenty-fifth percentile of the ability range for mathematics. The activities in the teaching programme were incorporated into the normal lesson and homework allocation of these pupils over a period of nine months. Their performance in a written test and some interviews was compared with pupils in two statistically similar control groups of pupils whose mathematical experience included little or no reference to proof.

The research was motivated by the fact that the author, a teacher with experience in secondary school classrooms spanning over thirty years, had witnessed the disappearance of proof, as exemplified by Euclidean geometry, and was concerned about the steady erosion of the importance of proof so that it rarely featured as part of the mathematics curriculum of most pupils in British secondary schools. Many textbooks stated mathematical facts and relationships with little or no justification. Although some included a section about proof this was usually an "extra" for able pupils and not an intrinsic part of the course. Additionally national examinations rarely featured an expectation of proof. They had wisely abandoned the testing of ability to rote learn proofs but had failed to replace this with an acceptable alternative. While pupils were assessed in coursework on their ability to search for and analyse patterns they were not expected to prove those relationships beyond the justification of an apparent number pattern.

The author, however, had continued to teach proof, albeit in an increasingly non-traditional way, reducing the emphasis on Euclidean proof and combining the notions of proof with problem-solving activities. The experience gained suggested that acceptance of an informal style of proof enabled more pupils to understand the notion of proof, and to construct their own proofs, without the constraints of an unfamiliar language in the early learning stages. Able pupils who become competent at this level can be extended by exposure to more formal proofs so that they might become familiar with the language used and begin to incorporate more formality into their own proofs. By including both informal and formal proof the needs of all pupils are addressed.

The author agrees with Ball's claim (1996) that teachers are responsible for providing pupils with experiences involving proof, and also Anderson's recommendation (1996) that teachers should encourage pupils to understand and produce proofs. In the opinion of the author the absence of proof impoverishes the mathematical experience of pupils, and the fact that methods of teaching it to date have not been appropriate for many pupils is not a valid reason for its neglect. It seems at least possible that shifting the emphases from the study of deductive, mainly formal, proofs to other more informal proofs might make ideas of proof accessible to more pupils. If proof activities include discrete items that pupils can see and count they are enabled at least to commence a proof with confidence, rather than the trepidation sometimes engendered by formal deductive proofs about unknown, continuously variable quantities, as in some geometry proofs. Some patterns suggest themselves as a possible framework in which to explore ideas of inductive, and other methods, of proof. The teaching programme used in the research was partially based on finding and explaining the structure of such patterns.

The pupils in the research study lacked experience in exploring patterns in mathematics and found some of the investigations more difficult than had been anticipated. Although most pupils in the experimental group were able to find correct formulae, some found explaining the structure of the patterns difficult, in some cases because they did not appreciate the structure and in others because they could not express their thoughts in words. However most pupils improved in their ability to understand and explain the structure of some patterns. Some of the more able pupils also improved in their ability to analyse a pattern in several ways. In the classroom it was possible to prove almost all formulae and geometric properties used and, in exceptional cases, to highlight the difference between proof and demonstration. Pupils were generally receptive to the notion of proving new mathematical ideas and, even for unusual and/or difficult proofs, most were interested and willing to take part in class discussion. The range of topics used in the teaching programme, to provide pupils of this age and ability with experience of proof, and the informal discussion-orientated approach adopted, were both appropriate.

The research teaching programme was successful in that the pupils in the experimental group learned to appreciate the notion of proof, and most could eventually prove in contexts involving visual patterns which led to number patterns. The emphasis, for these pupils, on explaining patterns and providing practice in recognising them, seemed to be at least as effective as the direct instruction in pattern-spotting techniques which had been given to pupils in one of two control groups. The fear that emphasising proof and pattern might adversely affect general mathematical attainment, due to consequent reduction in emphasis on practice, was unfounded. Statistical analyses of test results in the research, and later informal comparisons of GCSE results provided evidence to this effect.

Research and success of the teaching programme indicate that teaching proof through pattern makes it accessible to able pupils aged fourteen to sixteen, and gave some of them obvious satisfaction. Although their ability to prove is limited, this is an advance on total ignorance of proof, and has not been at the expense of progress in other areas of mathematics.

Design of the teaching programme

It is important that developing concepts of proof is incorporated into the mathematics teaching programme for all pupils. Proof should not be taught as a distinct aspect of mathematics but in such a way that it creates a unified and coherent mathematics curriculum.

The teaching programme advocated in this book aims to take full advantage of all opportunities to include proof in school mathematics and also to design additional material to give experience in pattern recognition and analysis. In the classroom the intention is to prove all formulae quoted and used (except on the rare occasions when the mathematics involved is too advanced) to ensure that all geometric properties are established by reasoned arguments based on known facts and properties (previously proven where appropriate), and to introduce pupils to situations which produce patterns appropriate for analysis. On those few occasions when proof is not appropriate the difference between demonstration or empirical evidence is highlighted.

The teaching programme may be incorporated into a school scheme of work based on the content of the English National Curriculum or any other curriculum. Within this framework it is broadly possible to adopt the teaching model for proof recommended by Reid (1996):

- build on students' innate ability to reason,
- help them formulate their own reasoning,
- include both explanation and exploration as rôles of proof".

The programme also takes into account the conditions recommended by Blum and Kirsch (1991) for teaching proof. These are:

- value many kinds of representations,
- frequently use "preformal proofs" in the classroom,
- give examples of formal proofs,
- formalise non-formal arguments,
- discuss proofs and proving.

It is recognised that all teachers are limited by practical constraints such as the school timetable and homework allocation, and size and composition of teaching groups. However teaching strategies, the selection of activities, and the order of introduction of mathematical content are mainly under the control of the teacher and can be varied according to their judgement.

The teaching strategies employed range from whole class exposition, and informal class discussion as advocated by Neubrand (1989), to working in small groups to share results and/or ideas about possible explanations, and also individual written work. The written work is sometimes based on structured questions and at other times open-ended questions or instructions are used. Although many investigations are based on analysing diagrams some are of a more practical nature, eg. measuring, and counting concrete objects. Some tasks are begun and completed during lessons, some begun in lessons and completed for homework, usually by writing a report of work done in class, some begun at home and then discussed in class, and a few shorter investigations set as a single homework task.

Variety in mathematical content is achieved by investigations based on number patterns which can be explained by use of algebra and/or diagrams, diagrams which can be analysed in terms of algebra, and spatial problems producing number patterns which are explained only in words. Anderson (1995) and Hewitt (1992) suggested that the recognition of pattern only is inadequate and should be followed by explanation. Porteous (1994) recommended that the rôle of proof can be enhanced by extending investigations and placing more emphasis on explaining patterns. Both these ideas are incorporated into this teaching programme.

The English National Curriculum includes knowledge and proof of some Euclidean properties. Whenever possible mathematical formulae should also be proved. This more formal aspect of proof should not be over-emphasised because this is not the same as teaching pupils to create their own proofs. Slomson (1996) observes further that the former does not help the latter, and advises against stressing the formality and rigour of proof. However it is necessary to include proofs in geometry and mensuration in order that pupils should not receive the "mixed message" that proof in one area of mathematics is expected but is not necessary in other areas. Additional advantages of including a variety of proof activities are that the range of proof methods is broadened, as advocated by Anderson and Austin (1995), and the body of content enriched as recommended by Gardiner (1995b). The advantage of pattern activities is that generally pupils find them easier to understand and thus they satisfy the need for accessible proof activities suggested by Anderson (1996).

Teachers will need to use their own discretion when assessing the rate of progress appropriate for a particular group of pupils as this is not specified in the teaching programme, which only attempts to suggest appropriate proof activities within a loosely ordered framework for each phase. At all times it is assumed that the class teacher is in the best position to judge when and how these activities might be used to maximum effect for a particular group of pupils. Such judgements are necessarily based on the teacher's knowledge of the age, ability, and interest of their pupils. For instance, in the short and medium term, teachers of older pupils who have not had prior experience of proof may need to telescope the programme of study but should try to incorporate as many of the Proof Discussions as possible even if they are only able to select a few of the Proof Activities.

The programme outlined below, and described in detail in the following three chapters, divides the teaching and learning of proof into three phases:-

1) pupils are introduced to the notion of proof;

2) pupils are introduced to the generalised nature of proof and challenged to construct simple proofs;

3) pupils are provided with a wide variety of proof opportunities, which introduce some elements of formal proof; and are expected to write more complex proofs.

These phases reflect the three categories of difficulties identified by Dreyfus et al (1990, p 129), after a summary of cognitive research about proof as experienced by high school students:−

- "a lack of the sense of the need for proof;
- a failure to grasp the nature of proof ......;
- difficulties in writing proofs".

The strategies for teaching proof implicit in the "Using and Applying" strand of the new English National Curriculum follow a similar progression to this with Key Stages 1 and 2 broadly comparable with the first phase:–

Key Stage 1 – lay foundations for proof (pp 38 and 39);

Key Stage 2 – use mathematical reasoning to explain (pp 42 and 43);

Key Stage 3 – understand the difference between a demonstration and a proof and show step-by-step deduction (pp 49 and 53);

Key Stage 4 (Higher Level) – derive proofs in algebra and progress towards full justification in more complex contexts in geometry (pp 68 and 72).

First Phase – Learning about proof

An awareness of the existence of proof is a vital pre-requisite to appreciating the need for proof and to constructing proofs. The awareness of pupils is raised by asking pupils for, and providing if necessary, explanations of both familiar, and then new mathematical ideas. It is recommended that, initially, teachers should direct short class discussions to justify previously accepted facts and properties as these are revisited/revised before they are extended into new areas. This questioning of previously accepted truths should be undertaken cautiously and sensitively. Teachers will be aware of the importance of not undermining pupils' confidence in the mathematics they can do by raising doubts in their minds before they are able to appreciate logical arguments.

During this phase pupils are likely to be taught angle facts in geometry. Although a few of these may, correctly, be presented as "generally accepted truths" or axioms, most should be explained using arguments based on the axioms, and the difference between axioms and proofs mentioned but not stressed at this stage. This is a difficult concept for all but the most able pupils. For most pupils the reasoning involved in explaining geometrical facts at this level will be informal, but for some it may be appropriate to introduce simple Euclidean proofs to explain, for instance, that vertically opposite angles are equal, and that angles of a triangle are supplementary.

As pupils become familiar with the idea that mathematical facts, properties, and procedures can be explained, they should be exposed to activities designed to culminate in explaining newly created (for the pupils) mathematics. Such activities could begin by investigating a "concrete situation" leading to simple number patterns which can be directly related to the structure of the original situation. After this stage is reached it would be unwise to provide activities which produce patterns or relationships which cannot be proved in terms that pupils can understand. Thus teachers who wish to investigate such questions as "How many squares are there on a chessboard?" should do so before any ideas of proof are introduced, or defer them until pupils are capable of either understanding the reasons for the resulting patterns or appreciating proof by exhaustion.

During this phase teachers should attempt to provide suitable proof or justification of all new mathematics taught. Such proofs are unlikely to be formal, even in geometry, but they should include a series of logical steps leading the pupils from the mathematics they understand to the new ideas being introduced. Although using an informal style these proofs should be mathematically correct at a level appropriate to the learners.

Chapter 2 includes suggestions for such proofs and how they might be presented to pupils. It also contains possible explanations for familiar mathematics and details of investigations leading to results which can be proved by, or with, pupils. Almost all pupils who have such proof experiences will become aware of the existence of proof and realise that checking a few cases is not proof and so attain Proof Level 2. Additionally many could learn to appreciate the need for proof and its generalised nature and thus attain Level 3. A few able pupils may learn to write simple proofs an so attain Level 4.

Second Phase – Learning to prove

By this stage pupils will have come to expect an explanation of how any new mathematics they learn is related to the mathematics they already understand. This will probably be achieved through teacher directed class discussions. However, it must be conceded that occasionally it may be necessary to admit to pupils that a proof exists but is beyond their level of understanding. Such occasions should be the exception rather than the rule, and proofs should then be replaced with demonstrations of truth, the difference between the two being highlighted. For instance, pupils who are taught to use Pythagoras'

Theorem without proof should at least be shown Perigal's dissection, with the explanation that it is merely a demonstration of truth for a given triangle.

In geometry some proofs will still be informal, but it may be appropriate to expose more pupils to formal Euclidean proofs of some basic geometric properties such those described above. Pupils are also more likely to appreciate the difference between assumptions and proofs when particular cases of these are drawn to their attention. As pupils progress they encounter more complex geometric facts and properties and an attempt should be made to explain all of these using either Euclidean proofs, or proofs based on geometric transformations, or informal reasoning such as transformational reasoning. Most pupils find constructing proofs in geometry difficult but, with practice, some are enabled to do so with minimal teacher intervention and begin to enjoy a feeling of achievement as they succeed.

Other areas of mathematics should be approached in a similar manner to geometry. Wherever possible a proof should be developed with the pupils through class discussion. The style of proof will vary depending on the age and ability of the pupils and the topic under consideration. For instance the basic formulae for areas and volumes ¢an still only be explained using informal inductive methods, but once these are established it is possible to derive most of the rest by formal deductive arguments. The occasions when proof is not possible provide opportunities to re-emphasise the difference between proof and demonstration.

During this phase it is possible to approach some of the formal mathematics prescribed by the National Curriculum, such as the angle sums for polygons, using investigations to produce results which may then be analysed and explained. Other proof activities appropriate at this stage will be mainly in "concrete" situations, as in the previous stage, but the results may be more complex such as those resulting in number patterns involving a quadratic relationship. Additionally analysis of some abstract number properties, such as divisibility tests, may also be appropriate for some pupils.

Suggestions for investigations at this stage are detailed in Chapter 3 and include one with a cross-curricular theme (mathematical analysis of the structure of hydrocarbons) and one in which a conjectured pattern fails, in order to reinforce the necessity for proof. The chapter also provides guidance on proving some new mathematics. The teaching material in this phase is intended to enable most pupils to appreciate the generalised nature of proof and and to write short proofs and so attain Proof Levels 3 or 4. A few very able pupils, who are able to write longer proofs, may approach Proof Level 5.

Third Phase – Improving proof skills

The suggestions in this section are mainly intended for able pupils in the last two years of compulsory schooling, but it is possible that some activities may be considered by the teacher to be appropriate for pupils of average ability, or for very able younger pupils.

Pupils at this stage are learning more complex mathematics and are also likely to be capable of exercising the logical reasoning processes necessary for understanding and/or creating proofs of more difficult mathematical concepts. For instance, their facility with algebra enables them to understand such proofs as that of the formula for solving quadratic equations, and their spatial ability is commensurate with that required to benefit from further exposure to some Euclidean proofs, involving an increasing degree of formality of style.

These pupils are also able to analyse more complex visual patterns which provide opportunities to compare different proof methods. They can also usefully be presented with examples of proofs requiring a significant shift in their line of thought, in order to gain an awareness that analysing apparently different structures can lead to similar results and that proof in one domain facilitates proof in another. One activity illustrating this is that Euler's relation for solid shapes is directly comparable with a similar result for networks. The purpose of such activities arises from the premise that the more unexpected connections pupils are exposed to, the more they are likely to appreciate the existence of unusual links and learn something of the fascination of mathematics.

Finally, able pupils older than about fourteen are able to acquire a deeper appreciation of the concept of proof *per se*. With exposure to different types of proof, such as proof by contradiction, they may increase their repertoire of proof methods and so become more proficient at constructing their own proofs. Although a formal approach to proof by induction is not recommended at this stage (some A-level pupils find this difficult) they may appreciate that there is a difference between an inductive and deductive proof. Some might benefit from treating Euclidean geometry as an example of an axiomatic system.

Towards the end of this stage it is useful to discuss various methods for establishing that angles in a triangle are supplementary. in order to reinforce the differences between demonstration, transformational reasoning, and formal deductive proof and to illustrate the power and precision of the latter in comparison with the former two. Such a discussion, and examples of appropriate proof activities are detailed in Chapter 4, and are intended to enable most pupils learning mathematics at this level to attain Proof Level 5.

Teaching strategies

For each phase there is a table after the "contents" listing the proofs for each phase with proof type, and also their associated proof levels. The only references to Levels 0 and 1 are with examples of "Not Proof" as pupils in classes discussing proofs can reasonably be expected to be aware of the existence of proof and to be unconvinced by one special case. The proof levels recorded in the first phase represent the expected attainment of most pupils in a class exposed to a particular proof activity or discussion. Levels are quoted as 2b/3 when both a generic example and a generalised proof have been considered because significant numbers of pupils are at each level. The levels associated with the proof activities in the second phase are affected by prior experience of pupils, and therefore by the order in which the activities are introduced. Some are quoted as 3/4 or 3/5 because some pupils will only understand a particular proof (Proof Level 3), some will be able to write a proof for a particular activity involving patterns (Proof Level 4), and some will demonstrate ability to write their own proofs on a number of occasions (Proof Level 5). Proof Level 5+ may be appropriate for pupils in the third phase who can compare proof methods, understand longer formal proofs, and also write their own proofs in a formal style.

Each of the following three chapters focuses on one phase and includes suggestions in varying degrees of detail for "Proof Discussions" about familiar and new (to pupils) mathematics, "Proof Activities" producing results to be proved, and "Not Proofs" including paradoxes and fallacies.

Proof discussions aim to blend ideas of proof with other aspects of the mathematics curriculum. They are mainly teacher instigated and directed but should always include pupil responses and on some occasions it may be possible to take advantage of a pupil comment or question to initiate class discussion. Many of the discussions in all three chapters are accompanied by diagrams to help clarify pupils' thinking. In Chapter 2 these diagrams are called "Picture Proofs" and in Chapter 4 they usually form part of a formal proof of a theorem. Although most proof discussions are likely to be short and embedded into lessons, a few may take more than thirty minutes, and so a summary of the discussion is included.

Proof Activities are based on the results of pupil investigations and begin with a worksheet explaining the "Pupil Challenge". In Chapter 2 the instructions in the worksheet are deliberately brief to avoid giving the impression that proving is difficult because it involves many words, and because it is assumed that the activity will be undertaken with the guidance of a teacher. Some pupils, especially those in primary schools, may find even the brief instructions difficult to follow independently. The challenge in this initial phase is to "Convince a friend!" in recognition of the fact that the proofs may be spoken, but not always written.

During the second phase, described in Chapter 3, pupils are challenged to "Convince a penfriend!" in order to encourage practice in writing proofs. Since pupils are less likely to be handicapped by difficulties in reading and writing the need for brevity is counter-balanced by a need for the support of more detailed instructions as pupils attempt to prove and write proofs independently. The pupil challenges in Chapter 4 expose pupils to more complex investigations about which they are expected to write full reports, to include proofs, mainly of explanations of patterns, in general terms.

Most proof activities are also accompanied by Lesson Outlines, which are brief summaries of teaching strategies involved. In Chapter 2 most of the lessons are planned in considerable detail, including step-by-step instructions, along with expected pupil responses, and some guidance on timing. In Chapter 3 the detailed instructions are replaced by descriptions of lessons, mainly with pupils in the experimental group in varying degrees of detail. Some proof activities are described through summaries of pupils' written reports, or responses in a written test, or through individual pupil interviews. Most of the pupil responses, both written and spoken, were from pupils in either the experimental or control groups in the research. In Chapter 4 there are Lesson Outlines for the first two proof activities and all others are described in a similar way to those in Chapter 3, except that the pupils involved also included some very able (top

10% of the ability range for mathematics) fifteen and sixteen year olds.

In each chapter there is then a section entitled "Not Proof". This includes examples of practical demonstrations, use of empirical evidence, fallacies and paradoxes. The purpose of the inclusion of these is to distinguish them from what is accepted as proof.

Finally, in each chapter, there are suggestions for assessment but in Chapters 2 and 3 they come with a large "health warning". In the opinion of the author there is little value in written assessment in the first phase for most pupils, and in the second it is unwise to isolate proof for assessment. If the tasks are not used for assessment purposes they are recommended for use as proof activities.

Proof in the sixth form

Because of the likelihood that for the foreseeable future pupils will enter sixth forms with little or no appreciation of proof, it would seem appropriate to consider how to introduce older students, to the notion of proof. For those studying A-level mathematics it is strongly recommended that this should be effected early in their course so that they learn to appreciate that proof is an intrinsic part of mathematics. It may also be possible to incorporate proof into courses for some other students. For instance, students who have elected to study other A-level subjects may be offered a course of proof in mathematics as part of a general studies course; and students who still need support to acquire basic mathematical skills might be enabled to forge new links in their understanding by the inclusion of proof of some elementary mathematical results.

All groups could benefit by exposure to some of the proof activities already suggested for younger pupils and other similar activities based mainly on patterns; and also by proof discussions of some previously accepted truths, including some traditional Euclidean proofs for the A-level students. Chapter 5 includes selections drawn from all three phases to create programmes of study to cater for the varying needs of students in the sixth form who have little, or no, prior experience of proof in mathematics.

All students studying A-level mathematics, and some following a general course, could also be introduced to examples of different types of proof. Additionally those studying A-level mathematics should be enabled to develop proofs for all the new ideas they are taught. They should also be given opportunities to construct proofs for themselves. Suggestions about which activities might be adapted for use with sixth form students and how proof might be integrated into an A-level mathematics course are included in Chapter 5.

Conclusion

The literature quoted in the first part of this chapter includes strong evidence to support the incorporation of proof into a school mathematics curriculum. It also includes several definitions of proof and descriptions of proof types, and also research findings about pupil understanding and perception of proof. The author's framework for describing pupils' development in this domain, using six levels, is based both on these findings and on personal research and classroom experience.

These six Proof Levels underpin the programme for teaching proof which is divided into three phases. The first phase teaches pupils about proof so that they understand the need for (Proof Level 1) and nature of (Proof Level 3) proof. The second phase builds on this understanding by increasing the degree of independence in writing about proof activities as they learn to prove (Proof Level 4). During the final phase, designed to cater for able pupils, they are exposed to a wider range of proof experiences, including more formal proof (Proof Level 5).

The following three chapters each focus on one phase and includes pupil worksheets and lesson plans for teachers. The fourth chapter includes three different selections of proof discussions and activities and explains how they might be used with older learners in Sixth forms and colleges.

CHAPTER 2

First Phase – Teaching and learning about proof

During this introductory phase of learning about proof, logical reasoning is used wherever possible to introduced new mathematics, and some familiar ideas are also justified through Proof Discussions. Proof Activities produce patterns and relationships whose justification involves use of oral explanation skills, as pupils are challenged to –
"Convince a friend!"

Introduction

The main purpose of teaching proof is that, as initial ideas about mathematical proof are introduced to pupils, they learn that mathematical statements can, and whenever possible should, be proved or explained. During this first phase pupils attain at least Proof Level 1. As they learn about the existence of proof through examples of proofs in the classroom, many will realise that checking a statement for one special case is insufficient as proof, and that either a special case should be treated as a generic example of a general statement or that more, varied or randomly selected, cases are considered. In other words many pupils can be expected to attain Proof Level 2.

The emphasis at this stage is on justifying number properties and patterns through generic examples ("action proofs" with diagrams) and geometry through transformational reasoning. However, able pupils will be capable of understanding the use of simple algebraic and geometric arguments as part of generalised proofs, and so may attain Proof Level 3. Repeated exposure to proofs or explanations will show pupils that new mathematical knowledge can be derived from familiar facts and properties, whatever their level of understanding of the detail of the proofs themselves. The emphasis here is on teaching an awareness of the existence of proof. Since this cannot be done in isolation, it may be that, during this phase, some pupils will only have a very superficial understanding of the essence of the arguments.

The next section describes class discussions to prove new (to pupils) and known mathematical properties. These are enhanced by diagrams called Picture Proofs where appropriate. Proof activities which give rise to patterns requiring explanations are then described, followed by some "Not Proofs". The fourth section discusses the appropriateness of assessment and suggests a task through which this might be achieved, if it is considered feasible and/or helpful.

Proof discussions with picture proofs

Ideally all new facts and properties to which pupils are introduced should be proved at an appropriate level, namely, using any mathematically correct reasoning that pupils can understand. Any facts and properties which cannot be proved should be deferred whenever possible. The teacher will need to exercise discretion here as to the depth of questioning possible with a particular group so that pupils do not lose confidence in what they already know, but rather gain confidence in the knowledge that all mathematics stands up to such analysis, albeit at this stage informal and in some cases somewhat superficial.

Proof discussions are not likely to form the major part of a lesson but are embedded into lessons which provide an appropriate context. Such discussions, suggestions for which are outlined in this section, are most likely to be instigated and directed by the class teacher, but should be significantly influenced by pupil contributions. These discussions should not be laboured and it is important to guard against pupils being involved in copying lengthy proofs or explanations. It is not essential at this stage that everything discussed be committed to paper in words. To do so might make the ideas seem more difficult to pupils. Wherever possible during this phase diagrams or apparatus, should be used.

Number

Discussions about the following number properties will probably be embedded into lessons practising basic number skills. There is no optimum order for the introduction of these properties and the proofs are unlikely to involve algebra at this stage.

Adding odd and even numbers

The addition of odd numbers provides a simple example of a proof. The result can be discovered by most pupils independently of the teacher. Some may be able to explain the result when prompted by suitable questioning and diagrams. The purpose of a discussion about adding two odd numbers is pupils understand a Picture Proof, similar to the one below.

ODD	+	ODD	→	EVEN
*****	+	***	=	********
****		****		********

Such a proof should be not presented as a "fait accompli", but pupils encouraged to work out their own explanations wherever possible.

A class discussion could be preceded by small group or paired discussions in which pupils are asked to consider means of representing odd numbers. It may be helpful for some pupils to use apparatus such as counters or cubes, although most should be capable of finding a pictorial representation. After a few minutes begin a class discussion by sharing ideas about this, probing where necessary, to elicit useful suggestions and to compare the merits of each. If diagrams have been used ask pupil volunteers to draw their ideas on the board, and if apparatus has been used ask some pupils to show their ideas to the class.

Pupils should then consider the result of adding pairs of odd numbers suggested by members of the class, and other pairs suggested by the teacher if necessary, by doing the numerical addition until they realise that all the results are even numbers. It is then appropriate to consider whether all pairs of odd numbers add to produce an even number; and to attempt an explanation. Most pupils will be confident that this always happens, and be surprised that any explanation is necessary! The rôle of the teacher here is crucial. It is necessary to highlight the benefit of a proof (absolute confidence in the result), while at the same time not creating uncertainty in the minds of pupils about the mathematics they thought they knew.

So now the result is accepted conditionally. The attention of the pupils is drawn back to the diagrams or apparatus as they are asked if any of them can see why it must always be true. If, as is likely, this is their first experience of proof any explanations will be in very informal language, possibly even colloquial, but if they have grasped the essence of an explanation pupils should be congratulated, and their style refined through class discussion. An acceptable explanation would be along the following lines:- "In even numbers all dots/counters/cubes can be paired. In odd numbers there is always an 'extra' dot/counter/cube. Two odd numbers have two extra dots/

counters/cubes and these make a pair. The result is therefore pairs of dots/counters/cubes, which make an even number."

A record of this discussion will require more than one diagram, accompanied by the relevant numerical addition. Only one example may give the misleading impression that the explanation is only valid for that particular case. Written verbal explanations at this stage are not helpful. In some classes it may be appropriate to continue a lesson by considering the addition of two even numbers, and then odd and even numbers, but it is unwise to labour discussions about these results.

Adding consecutive odd numbers

It is not uncommon for even older, able pupils to fail to recognise a sequence of square numbers on sight, but to recognise instead that the difference between successive terms are odd numbers. Such pupils may or may not then recognise the square numbers. An example of an able fifteen year old girl who struggled to identify 1, 4, 9, 16, as the first four square numbers is described in Chapter 4. Considering the reverse problem described here may prevent such difficulty. This property can be discovered by pupils and an explanation elicited through a class discussion based on the following diagrams:–

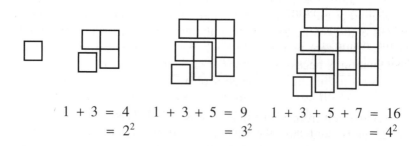

$$1 + 3 = 4 \qquad 1 + 3 + 5 = 9 \qquad 1 + 3 + 5 + 7 = 16$$
$$= 2^2 \qquad\qquad = 3^2 \qquad\qquad\qquad = 4^2$$

It may be necessary to consider an inverse example, like removing 2^2 from 3^2 to give the third odd number, diagrammatically before the method of "building" square numbers is appreciated. On a different occasion the following property can also be presented. The "double staircase" shows square numbers as the sum of consecutive triangle numbers.

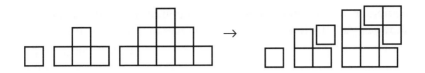

Adding consecutive integers from 1

This can be presented to pupils as a challenge to, say, add the integers from 1 to 50 (an even number in the first instance) and time allowed for completion by any method, before a class discussion to compare and analyse methods. Alternatively, to avoid some pupils spending a long time on simple arithmetic, the emphasis can be placed from the outset on a search for a short-cut. This would be a better approach for able pupils. In both cases a class discussion could be preceded by an opportunity for pupils to share ideas in pairs or small groups. As even able pupils are unlikely to find a short-cut without teacher intervention the time allowed for these discussions should be only a few minutes. (Some teachers may prefer to postpone this problem until pupils are more likely to solve it independently.) There are two conceptually different ways of analysing this problem and, although both may not arise naturally out of the discussion, both have value.

Begin a discussion by asking pupils whether they prefer to write out the sum in figures, or to find an alternative representation, and proceed by following up their suggestions. If the majority prefer figures, or none can think of an alternative, write an abbreviated sum on the board and, if possible, elicit the suggestion of pairing from each end of the sum as shown below:–

$$1 + 2 + 3 + \ldots + 24 + 25 + 26 + 27 + \ldots + 48 + 49 + 50$$

Try to elicit from pupils that for this sum each pair is 51 and there are 25 pairs, and thus the total is 25×51, and then, if possible, attempt to generalise using words, e.g. multiply one more than the last integer by half the number of integers. The algebraic equivalent $\frac{n}{2}(n + 1)$ may be appropriate in classes of able pupils.

It may be possible to elicit an appropriate diagrammatic representation from a pupil by asking them for a means of representing numbers which increase in equal steps in the hope that a staircase, or similar, is suggested. Ask pupils to consider the practical difficulty of illustrating the first fifty integers and then to suggest a viable (smaller) alternative. Try to make it clear that both are particular cases representing the general case. Suitable diagrams showing the addition of the first ten integers is shown below:–

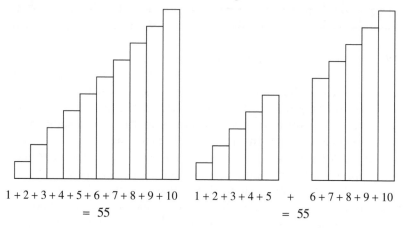

$1 + 2 + 3 + 4 + 5 + 6 + 7 + 8 + 9 + 10$ $1 + 2 + 3 + 4 + 5$ + $6 + 7 + 8 + 9 + 10$

$= 55$ $= 55$

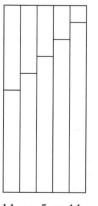

$$\tfrac{10}{2} \times 11 = 5 \times 11 = 55$$

Depending on the ability and interest of the pupils it may be appropriate to continue by considering how the methods would need to be modified for an odd numbers of integers. If this is done algebraically it will be necessary to use $\tfrac{1}{2}(n + 1)n$ and ideally discuss the mathematical equivalence to, but structural difference from, the previous version.

Pupils who have considered this problem usually enjoy the (apocryphal?) story about Gauss who, as a ten-year-old boy, deprived his teacher of a few minutes respite. He solved this problem, which was expected to keep him occupied for some time, in a very few minutes using a short-cut like these.

Divisibility tests

Some pupils will be aware of some divisibility tests but, like those who are not, will probably not have considered why they work. Pupils could work in small groups to search for tests for 10, 5, 2, and 9 (in that order), before a class discussion to establish explanations. Discussion about multiples of ten will involve reference to, and possibly a reason for, the fact that ten is the basis of the denary counting system. It may be appropriate in some classes to present this is an axiom, or agreed convention, of mathematics. Multiples of five and two are easily recognised by pupils and many are likely to be able to explain the tests in terms of multiples of ten.

Multiples of nine, even up to only 99, are less likely to be recognised. The test that the sum of the digits is nine or a multiple of nine is unlikely to be explained by pupils. An explanation along the lines indicated by the following diagrams will at least demonstrate to pupils that there is a reason, even if they do not fully understand the reasoning.

$$63 \ = \ 6 \times 10 + 3 \ = \ 6 \times 9 + 6 \times 1 + 3 \ = \ 6 \times 9 + 9 \ = \ 7 \times 9$$

Digit sum
= 6 + 3
= 9

Whether or not other multiples of nine, or numbers which are not divisible by nine are considered, will again depend on the age and interest of the pupils. In some classes it may be appropriate to consider a divisibility test for three and then six (test for two and three), but only if the explanation is likely to be understood by pupils.

A related question, possibly worth considering in some classes, is why the first ten multiples to nine can be shown using the fingers on both hands, as illustrated below:–

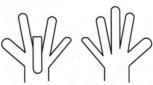

This example, with the third finger down, shows $3 \times 9 = 27$, since there are two fingers to the left of the third finger $(2 \times 10 = 20)$ and seven to the right $(20 + 7 = 27)$. Interviews with pupils in the experimental group of the research (Chapter 1) indicated that they could not explain this without teacher intervention. It is therefore unlikely that pupils in this phase of learning about proof will spontaneously be able to explain this. An explanation along the lines outlined in the previous paragraph will again at least show that there is an explanation, which is an important lesson about proof.

Commutativity of addition and multiplication

Diagrams like those below point towards the proof of the commutativity of addition and multiplication. One way of minimising the risk that pupils think that one such example proves each of these properties is to encourage them to draw their own Picture Proofs and share ideas.

$3 + 2 = 5$

$2 + 3 = 5$

Three rows of four
$3 \times 4 = 12$

Four rows of three
$4 \times 3 = 12$

Lengthy discussions about these are of little value as pupils find the ideas difficult to express in words. For most pupils $6 \times 3 = 3 \times 6$ "because it just does"! In this instance a few minutes spent considering diagrams similar to those above, drawn on the board, along with some pupil suggestions, would suffice to convey the message that there is a reason for these properties of numbers. In primary classrooms lines of pupils could be used to demonstrate the commutativity of addition, and arrays of bricks or counters for multiplication.

Area

Rectangles

A discussion about areas of rectangles with older pupils inexperienced in proof is described in Chapter 3 with associated diagrams. Ideally such a discussion should take place with younger pupils when they first encounter the concept of area. Once they understand that area is the space inside, or taken up by, a flat shape, and that one unit for measuring it is square centimetres, they should be given the opportunity for practical work involving tiling, or drawing on centimetre squared paper. Provided that all rectangles at this stage have integer dimensions pupils discover that 'Area = length × width'. Class discussion to explain this result will be based on the need to multiply the number of squares in rows and columns to find the total.

Further discussion could consider areas of rectangles with non-integer dimensions, such as 5½cm by 3½cm. This is only recommended if pupils are familiar with millimetres and converting units of area. Some pupils may suggest that this area would be 5 × 3 cm² plus an extra little square (½ × ½) cm², but this misunderstanding is resolved by asking pupils to draw the rectangle on centimetre squared paper. They realise there are also two smaller rectangles to take into account, and also that finding and adding four separate areas may not be the best method for finding the total area. Converting the dimensions to millimetres and considering tiling with millimetre squares is a better method. Pupils who know that 100mm² = 1 cm² can compare this result in square centimetres with 5.5 × 3.5. This generic example justifies acceptance of the formula for non-integer dimensions.

If pupils then do areas of other rectilinear figures any discussions should be preceded by practical work with dissections to create rectangles from triangles and parallelograms. These are considered in the next chapter.

Geometry

Most geometry at this level relates to basic angle properties/facts and can either be explained in terms of transformational reasoning, or through use of basic algebra in simple deductive proofs. Although the use of language is informal, reference is made to agreed facts, or axioms, and although plane Euclidean geometry is assumed during most of this work the possibility of other geometries is raised.

Angles at a point

It is necessary to start work on angles with the assumption, or axiom, that angles at a point add up to 360°. Pupils are interested in the fact that this originated with the Babylonians who based their number system on the number sixty, and discussion about this, asking pupils to suggest possible advantages of 360 (a large number which produces appropriately sized unit, and has many factors), is recommended. Pupils could perhaps be encouraged to find out more about the Babylonian, or other number systems, either in books or on the Internet.

Angles on a straight line

Once pupils are familiar with the idea that angles at a point sum to 360° they may be able to explain why angles on a straight line sum to 180°. It is certainly worth asking them, but if they cannot do so satisfactorily they are likely to be able to appreciate that the turn involved from facing one way along a line to facing the opposite way is half a complete turn. Discussions along these lines involve elements of deductive and transformational reasoning.

Right-angles

Pupils will probably learn to recognise a right-angle visually before they are concerned about measurement. As they learn about measuring angles, right-angles are defined as one quarter of a complete turn. Pupils can then calculate (prove) a right-angle is 90° and check by measuring known right-angles, such as those on squared paper. They could be reminded that checking is not proving. The term "perpendicular" to describe two lines at right-angles to each other could be introduced here.

Vertically opposite angles

The equality of vertically opposite angles can be explained, with the aid of two straight rods to represent straight lines, and an argument based on transformational reasoning. Whichever position the rods are held in (pupils can be asked to do this), the sum of any adjacent pair of angles is 180° and one angle is common to each pair. Discussion along the same lines with a diagram to replace the rods leads naturally to a deductive proof, which ideally will involve the use of simple algebra, but this is not essential for understanding the geometry. The following three proofs range from one with no algebra and only four different words, to a Euclidean proof with algebra.

Proof 1
Line 1

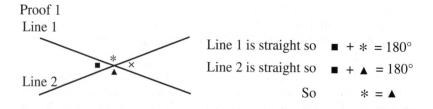

Line 1 is straight so   ■ + ✳ = 180°
Line 2 is straight so   ■ + ▲ = 180°

So   ✳ = ▲

Proof 2

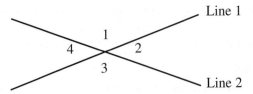

Angle 1 + Angle 2 = 180° (Line 1 is straight)
Angle 3 + Angle 2 = 180° (Line 2 is straight)
Angle 1 + Angle 2 = Angle 3 + Angle 2 = 180°
Angle 1 = Angle 3
Similarly   Angle 2 = Angle 4
Vertically opposite angles are equal.

Proof 3

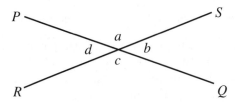

$a + b = 180°$ (angles on straight line PQ)
$c + b = 180°$ (angles on straight line RS)

$$a + b = c + b = 180°$$

$$a = c \quad \text{(subtract } b\text{)}$$

Similarly $b = d$
Vertically opposite angles are equal.

Angles and parallel lines

A suitable starting point for a discussion about angles in parallels is to ask pupils to describe them. The response that parallel lines are in the same direction provides justification for the fact that corresponding angles are equal. The related facts that alternate angles are equal and interior (or allied) angles are supplementary can then be deduced.

In some classes reference to the fact that agreed definitions, or axioms, form the basis of plane Euclidean geometry may be appropriate. For able or older pupils, unlikely to be confused by an apparent contradiction, consideration of the fact that two people walking north , i.e. in apparently parallel directions, from different points of the equator will eventually meet could be used to raise awareness of other geometries, such as spherical geometry.

Angles in a triangle

The fact that angles in a triangle sum to 180° can be demonstrated, explained, or proved in several different ways. Pupils should be exposed to some or all of the following:–

a) measuring and summing angles in several triangles

b) demonstration by tearing off and rearranging corners

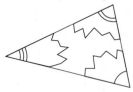

Since a) is likely to incur errors of measurement and addition and both a) and b) are demonstrations and not proof, these should not be the only approach for most pupils. The following three explanations are preferred to the demonstrations because they are based on transformational reasoning (Simon, 1996, pp 197-210). The previous activities lead to an awareness that the angles of some triangles seem to sum to about 180°, and no pupil in a class finds an exception. However pupils are essentially taking on trust the teacher's claim that the angle sum for all triangles is exactly 180°. The arguments based on transformational reasoning are more likely to lead pupils to an "intuitive conviction" (Fischbein, 1982, pp 9-18) that the result applies to all triangles.

c) "rotating" corners (Hewitt, 1996, MT155, p28)

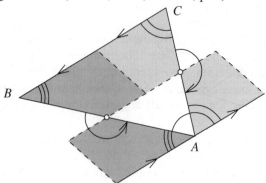

If this method is used it would be advisable to either provide pupils with a printed copy or prepare in advance a diagram on the board or for an overhead projector.

d) rotating ruler through each angle in turn

When this is demonstrated to pupils, it is important they appreciate that the sense of rotation of the ruler remains constant, and also that the ends of the ruler are identified before and after rotation. Pupils can then observe that the ruler rotates through a half turn, which they have proved is 180°.

e) hinged rods

 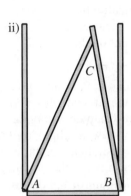

The rods are hinged, or moved as if they are hinged. Pupils can be involved in holding the rods and moving them as instructed by the teacher. Initially i) the longer rods are perpendicular to the base rod and so angles A and B sum to 180°. When two vertical rods are inclined towards each other until they meet ii), angle C has "gained" what A and B have "lost", and thus the total remains constant at 180°.

f) tessellation of triangles – without, or with, algebra

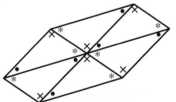

At each "node" we have a complete turn

$$\times \; * \; \bullet \; \times \; * \; \bullet \; = \; 360°$$

Dividing both sides by 2 gives

$$\times \; * \; \bullet \; = \; 180°$$

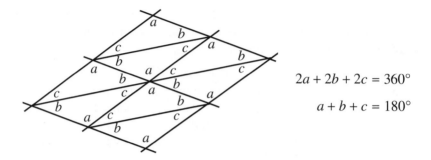

$$2a + 2b + 2c = 360°$$

$$a + b + c = 180°$$

Technically this is the converse of the theorem that triangles tessellate because their angles are supplementary, but it is an improvement on the "proof" by tearing off corners.

g) Euclidean proof

For older or very able younger pupils the deductive proof below, based on the hinged rods approach, or one of the deductive proofs included in Chapter 3 may be appropriate. One way of deriving this proof is to draw the lines on the board and ask a pupil volunteer to add marks to indicate equal angles. Another pupil could be asked to provide reasons for the equality of the angles. Then ask the class to compare the sum of the original angles with the sum of the angles in the triangle. The following diagram shows the equal angles but is not a complete proof because it does not include the spoken contributions of the pupils.

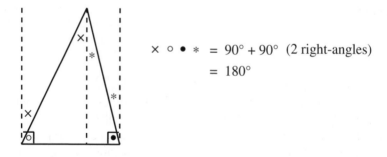

$$\times \, \circ \, \bullet \, * \; = 90° + 90° \;\; (2 \text{ right-angles})$$

$$= 180°$$

A more formal, algebraic approach to this is indicated below.

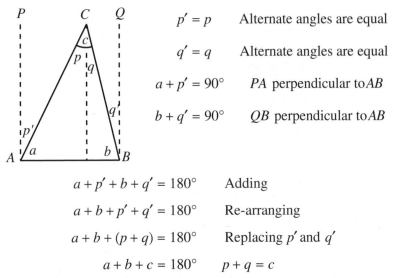

$p' = p$	Alternate angles are equal
$q' = q$	Alternate angles are equal
$a + p' = 90°$	PA perpendicular to AB
$b + q' = 90°$	QB perpendicular to AB

$$a + p' + b + q' = 180° \quad \text{Adding}$$

$$a + b + p' + q' = 180° \quad \text{Re-arranging}$$

$$a + b + (p + q) = 180° \quad \text{Replacing } p' \text{ and } q'$$

$$a + b + c = 180° \quad p + q = c$$

Whichever of these proofs is selected it should be developed through class discussion and not presented to pupils as a "fait accompli".

Probability

The tension between pupils' intuitive ideas about probability and correct understanding is familiar to teachers. The discussion here attempts to reconcile the discrepancy between pupils' estimate of a probability and its correct value, by both experimental observation and reasoned argument.

One event

Once pupils have understood the concept of probability and realise the advantages of assigning numerical values they can consider the simple event of tossing a coin. Class discussion about possible outcomes and associated probabilities should include "equally likely" ideas and then an estimate that the probability of (say) heads is a half. The reason behind this need not be explained to the pupils at this stage. Instead pupils should decide how many times they need to toss a coin in order to find the probability by experiment, and then carry out the experiment. Class discussion of the results would seem to confirm the result of 0.5, but at this point it is still a conjecture. Consideration of theoretical probability, as one way to get heads compared with two different outcomes, then proves the result.

Two events

As pupils first encounter the various outcomes when two coins are tossed they have no difficulty in identifying three different outcomes, namely, two heads, one head or no heads (or equivalents). Begin a class discussion about this by asking pupils for the possible outcomes and listing them on the board. Then consider the likelihood of each and how the probabilities might be quantified; or if pupils are familiar with the use of fractions for this, ask them to suggest values for the probabilities of the outcomes listed on the board. It is highly likely that at least one pupil will suggest that the probability of both heads (or any of the listed outcomes) is one third, and that no pupil will know the correct value.

At this point the need for experimental evidence is appreciated by the pupils and they should be given the opportunity for this and told to keep a tally for each of the three different outcomes. They should collect results until most realise that the original conjecture is incorrect. During the subsequent discussion several results could be combined to calculate the experimental probability of two heads. Pupils will modify their conjecture to $p = \frac{1}{4}$. The fact that this is still a conjecture should be emphasised, and the need for proof highlighted.

A theoretical proof can be developed by using a possibility space diagram to identify the four equally likely outcomes, along with the definition of expected theoretical probability, thus:–

		1st coin	
2nd	H	HH	HT
coin	T	TH	TT

$$\text{Expected probability} = \frac{\text{Number of successful outcomes}}{\text{Number of equally likely different outcomes}}$$

This examination of all cases to confirm the correct result is a simple example of a proof by exhaustion.

Proof Activities

Once pupils are familiar with the notion of proof they can be exposed to the idea that they might create their own proofs. Although they are unlikely to be able to do this in the domain of formal mathematics, some pupils may be able to explain the structure of patterns arising out of investigations. However most are unlikely to be able to do this in writing unaided. In this chapter there are references to use of algebra to describe patterns. This is not an essential part of the activities and may be inappropriate for many pupils.

The emphasis in the proof activities in this section is on finding and then explaining patterns. This will mainly be by discussion. Such investigations are also appropriate at this level because they help pupils acquire skills necessary for problem-solving. It may therefore be advisable to concentrate on strategies for problem-solving in some early investigations, and not to introduce notions of proof simultaneously. However once the notion of proof has been introduced to pupils it is important to try to explain the results of all investigations, and therefore to select only those investigations in which this is possible. Although the investigations are instigated by the class teacher the proof discussions arise naturally in the process of finding and explaining patterns.

Inductive arguments are likely to be used to establish results for most of the activities in this section, but these arguments should be followed by a deductive argument to explain the pattern wherever possible. However some pupils, especially those with a distinct bias towards geometry, may be able to side-step the induction stage. The activities about lines of lollipops and reversing digits may involve deduction based on a particular case as a generic example. The last two activities, based on choosing three objects from five, is designed to involve proof by exhaustion.

These investigations should not be completed in quick succession, but be introduced intermittently over a period of time spanning both primary and secondary education. The first three activities and the ninth, "A new team strip", are designed with the interests of primary school pupils in mind. The eighth activity, "Handshakes", and the tenth, "Dot-to-dot triangles", are recommended for use in secondary schools. The remainder could be used in either primary or secondary schools, depending on the ability, interest and proof experience of the pupils. Teachers in secondary schools could start with the fourth proof activity, "Intersecting circles", or use any, or all, of the first three as a simpler introduction.

The order of the remaining investigations, and whether or not additional investigations are carried out, is left to the discretion of the teacher. Only the teacher in the classroom is in a position to judge when and how best to introduce them to a particular group of pupils. Pupil worksheets are included but their use is not essential as the teacher will be introducing and guiding the investigations and discussions. Some pupils, especially those in primary schools, will find even these brief instructions difficult to interpret without such guidance. Each of the following investigations will probably form a substantial part of a lesson, but some may take less than half an hour. The investigation about "Handshakes" may require more than one hour.

The Lesson Plans are intended to support those teachers who have not used this approach before. They include:–

- practical guidance about how to start,
- important discussion points and
- suggested blends of class discussion and individual or small group work.

The expected outcomes include:–

- explanations for each pattern,
- some guidance on timing initially,
- the appropriateness of pupils' written reports,
- the degree of assistance likely to be necessary for these.

The salient features of each lesson plan are printed in bold type, and are also included in brief summaries – Lesson Outlines – at the beginning of each activity. Indication of timing can only be very approximate as circumstances in classrooms are extremely variable.

Pupils are likely to offer unexpected responses in class discussions, and teachers will take advantage of these. Discussion about incorrect responses provides opportunities to resolve difficulties and reinforce correct explanations. Alternative correct responses play an important rôle in demonstrating that the existence of several valid explanations is a frequent occurrence in mathematics. As these explanations will be valued by the teacher, pupils will gain in confidence in offering their own explanations. Some of the following activities produce results with more than one correct explanation.

Pupil Challenge

Bricklaying

Bricks are laid in lines with cement to join them.
How many joins for a line of bricks?

Find out for some short lines.
Look for a pattern.
Try to describe it.
Can you explain it?

Convince a friend

This is an example of a single operation (subtract one) number relationship, set in a visual real-life context. The number of bricks is deliberately not specified, in order to encourage pupils to think in general terms rather than about particular cases. It is expected that the class teacher will introduce this activity by explaining how to interpret the open numerical question, and asking pupils why they are advised to start with short lines. Pupils need not have a copy of the worksheet.

Lesson Outline (20-30 minutes)

Bricklaying

1. Explain the task. Discuss modelling.
2. Discuss how to start.
3. Provide materials and tell pupils to solve problem for 1, 2, and 3 bricks.
4. Ask pupils what they have found out. Record in table on board.
5. Explain that there is insufficient evidence. Pupils to continue collecting results.
6. Ask volunteers to add results to table.
7. Ask pupils to describe pattern.
8. Justify need for explanation. Ask pupils for theirs.
(9. Written reports only if appropriate.)

Lesson Plan

1. **Explain the task** to the pupils and clarify that they will need to choose the numbers of bricks. If the worksheet is used with primary pupils, teachers will need to check the instructions, and re-word them if necessary. **Discuss** with pupils what **materials/ apparatus** they could use to model this problem.

    One way is plastic bricks joined with plasticine, but there are equally good alternatives, such as drawing on squared paper.

2. **Discuss** with pupils how they will **start** the investigation.

    If this is the pupils' first experience in looking for number patterns they will need to realise the advantages of starting with one brick and then adding one at a time. Try to elicit this suggestion from pupils.

3. Organise pupils to work in pairs or small groups. **Provide materials/apparatus** or squared paper. Tell pupils to **find how many joins for up to three bricks**, by making models or drawing.

    This will not take very long. Allow a few pupils to consider four bricks if they finish early, but discourage them from guessing on the basis of continuing the number pattern.

4. **Stop practical work** and and **ask pupils what they have found** out. Allow one or two to tell the class their results. Ask them how they could **record this.**

    Try to elicit the suggestion of tabulating and complete the table on the board below with results from a different pupil.

Number of bricks	Number of joins
1	0
2	1
3	2

5. **Explain that that there is insufficient evidence** here to be able to make reliable predictions or draw safe conclusions. Pupils should **continue** practical investigation, and record their results.

    At this stage a few pupils may feel sure they know the answer. Tell them they can either collect more results to confirm what they know or consider how to explain why they know.

6. **Stop practical work** when most pupils have results for five or six bricks. Ask for **volunteers** to **add** their **results to the table** on the board. Ask some others if they agree with the values.

There are unlikely to be problems at this stage but it is important to resolve any that do occur until all pupils accept the values on the board.

7. Ask **pupils** if they can **describe how the number of joins is related to the number of bricks.**

    The most likely response is "one less," but some pupils may have other ways of expressing this. A few pupils may be able to express it algebraically as $j = b - 1$ where j and b represent the number of joins and bricks respectively.

8. **Explain** that even though this rule works for the lines of bricks made/drawn so far, **we need to know why** it works before we can assume it can be applied to longer lines.

    Ask pupils if they can explain why the rule should always work.

    Responses should be along the lines indicated below:–

    * The first brick on its own does not need any cement/have a join. The number of bricks with joins is one less than the total number of bricks. This is the same as the number of joins.

or * In laying a line of bricks there is no need for cement on the last brick because there is not a new brick to join on. Counting the number of joins is the same as counting all but the last brick. So the number of joins is the number before the number of bricks.

    Ask several pupils for their version. Encourage full precise responses and always ask other pupils if they can suggest improvements. Although pupils may find this embarrassing at first, it is important that they learn to share the development of proofs. They also learn that full explanations are necessary and so partial answers need to be improved.

9. If a **written report** is required it need only include a copy of the table of results, a sentence like "The number of joins is one less than the number of bricks" and an explanation similar to those above. Most pupils working at this level will find writing this difficult. It is not essential for learning about proof.

    For many pupils, especially younger ones, written reports might leave them with a negative feeling about this work. A positive interest in learning about proof is far more important at this stage than writing about it.

Pupil Challenge

A rose hedge

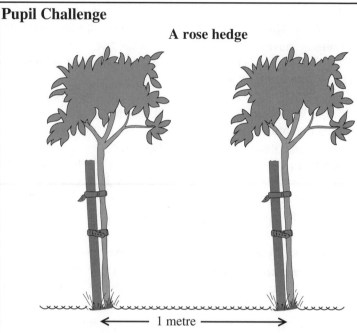

←——— 1 metre ———→

Rose trees are planted one metre apart to make a hedge.
How many rose trees are needed?

Find out for some short hedges.
Look for a pattern.
Try to describe it.
Can you explain it?

Convince a friend.

This activity is very similar to the previous one, and again teachers in primary schools are advised to check the instructions in the worksheet if they issue it to pupils. As before, the deliberate omission of specific numbers will need to be explained. The only differences are that the pattern is "one more" rather than "one less", and the problem includes units of length. Neither of these increases significantly the level of difficulty. The only differences in the lesson plan are that bricks become metres, and joins become rose trees. This has a negligible effect on the Lesson Outline and so this is not repeated. Only modelling at Stage 1 and responses at Stages 7 and 8 are included here.

Lesson Plan

1. Counters or plastic bricks can be used to represent rose trees, unless pupils have more imaginative ideas which are also practicable. If pupils are not familiar with ideas of scale any suitable fixed length, such as a pencil, can be used for one metre spacing. Pupils capable of using scale and measuring can place rose trees at 10cm intervals.

2-6 and 9. See previous Lesson Outline.

7. For a few pupils the relationship one more might be expressed algebraically as $r = m + 1$ where r and m are the number of rose bushes and metres respectively.

8. Correct explanations should include reference to:–

   - The number of spaces is the same as the number of metres.

   and • Either the first rose does not create a space, or an extra rose is needed at the end.

   and • The number of roses is one more that the number of spaces.

   and • The number of roses is one more than the number of metres in the length of the hedge.

   If a pupil makes a comment about the space taken up by a rose tree the teacher could point out that for the planted twigs this can be ignored but that as the trees grow the distance between them will get less.

Pupil Challenge

Lollipop lines

Some red lollipops are placed in a line.

Then some green lollipops are placed between the red ones.

How many lollipops are there altogether?

Find out for some short lines of lollipops.
Look for patterns.
Try to describe them.
Can you explain them?

Convince a friend.

Since one interpretation of this pattern involves adding odd and even numbers it is preferable if pupils have previously discussed this (earlier in this chapter). It is more difficult than the previous two activities because there are two steps to explain why the totals are odd numbers. One of these is the same as the relationship in the first activity. Some pupils will also be able to consider exactly which odd number for a particular case. Not all will be able to generalise the result.

As with the previous two activities, pupils are not expected to work independently from this worksheet. Most will need teacher support to understand the instructions, in particular how to interpret "some" and "short". They will also need guidance about how to start the investigation. Since the lesson plan will be essentially the same as for the previous two activities at Stages 2 to 6 it is not described in detail except for the table of results at Stage 4. Stages 7 to 11 are about finding and explaining several patterns and relationships. Stages 12 and 13, concerning use of algebra and written reports, are optional.

Lesson Outline (about 30 minutes)
Lollipop lines

1. Explain the task. Discuss modelling.
2. Discuss how to start.
3. Provide materials and tell them to solve problem for 1, 2, and 3 red lollipops.
4. Ask pupils what they have found out. Record in table of three columns on board.
5. Explain that there is insufficient evidence. Pupils to continue collecting results.
6. Ask volunteers to add results to table for up to 5 or 6 red lollipops.
7. Ask pupils to describe pattern (+1) and connection (-1) for green lollipops.
8. Justify need for explanation. Ask pupils for theirs. (Reminder – "Bricklaying").
9. Ask pupils to describe patterns in the total number of lollipops (odds, +2).
10. Ask pupils to explain these.
11. Summarise findings so far.
    Discuss total for, say, 20 red lollipops (39 = 20th odd number).
    (Generalise if appropriate.)
(12. Algebra if appropriate $- r + (r + 1)$, or $2(r - 1) + 1$, or $2r - 1$.)
(13. Written reports if appropriate.)

Lesson Plan

1. In order to **explain the task** either show pupils lines of lollipops, or draw some on the board. Start with four red ones, then add three green ones in the spaces. Explain that these numbers were chosen for convenience and that pupils will need to investigate for different numbers of lollipops.

    Discuss what they could use **to represent lollipops**.

    Counters, bricks, drawing and colouring, or painting are suitable, but pupils may suggest more imaginative alternatives. Encourage this and use their ideas if practicable.

2-3. See above.

4.   Results for first three red lollipops, to be suggested by pupils.

Number of red lollipops	Number of green lollipops	Total number of lollipops
1	0	1
2	1	3
3	2	5

5-6. See above.

7.   When the table of results on the board has been completed by
     pupil volunteers for up to five or six red lollipops remind them
     that they chose the starting number of red lollipops. Tell them
     there are **several other number patterns and connections. Ask
     them to describe any** they can see relating to **green** lollipops.

     Expected responses are:–

     • The number of green lollipops increases by one at a time.

     • The number of green lollipops is one less than the number
       of red ones.

     Write these suggestions briefly as +1 and −1 at appropriate
     positions on the table.

     If pupils are unable to suggest these without prompting point to
     the relevant lines, or pairs of numbers in the table, and ask for a
     fact about the number of green lollipops, a connection between
     the number of green lollipops and the number of red ones

8.   **Remind** pupils that **explanations** are necessary in order to be
     certain that the patterns continue.

     Ask them if they can explain either of the suggestions above. A
     reminder to think back to the activity **"Bricklaying"** might be
     appropriate.

     Responses should be along the lines indicated below:–

     • Every additional red lollipop, after the first, creates a
       space for an extra green one.

     • The number of spaces is one less than the number of red
       lollipops (like the number of joins in a line of bricks).

9.   Ask pupils to **describe any patterns in the total** number of
     lollipops.

Expected responses are:–
- The total number of lollipops is always an odd number.

or • The total number of lollipops increases by two from one.
Write these briefly on the board as odds, +2, at appropriate positions on the table. At this point do not try to elicit the relationship between the total and the number of red lollipops. If a pupil offers such a suggestion explain that it will be discussed later.

10. **Ask pupils if they can explain** either of the facts about the total number of lollipops.

Responses should include reference to:–
- when one number is one less then another one of them is odd and the other even,
- the sum of an odd and even number is always an odd number,
- when a new red lollipop is added a green one is put in the new space created, adding two new lollipops to the total.

This explains how and why the pattern continues, but does not explain how to find the total number of lollipops for a given number of red ones. However, only continue discussion about this if pupils are still actively involved. In some classes this might be an appropriate point at which to conclude the discussion on this occasion and return to it later to complete the explanation.

11. Ask pupils to **summarise** the findings so far. Remind them that, although the total number of lollipops has been shown to be an odd number, they have not yet considered which odd number gives the total for, say, **twenty red lollipops. Ask them if they could explain how to do this.**

A pupil may suggest the total is 20 + 19 (because it is one less) = 39. Ask them if they can say which odd number this is. It may be necessary to prompt in order to elicit the correct response (20th). Ask them if they can **explain** this.

It may be necessary to consider smaller numbers before they are able to explain for twenty.

Use pupil suggestions to develop at least one of the following explanations:–
- The total, 20+19=39 (see above), is the same as one less than two twenties, which is the 20th even number. Odd

numbers are before even numbers (eg. 1 before 2) and so the total is the 20th odd number.

- All but one red lollipop (first or last) can be paired with a green one, so the total is one more than 2×19, or the next number after the 19th even number, which is the 20th odd number.

- If a green lollipop is placed after every red one there would be 20 pairs of lollipops in the total, which is the 20th even number. There is no green lollipop after the last red one so the actual total is the number before the 20th even number, which is the 20th odd number.

These explanations are based on twenty lollipops as a generic example and so is a proof at Proof Level 2b. For many pupils this may be an appropriate point at which to conclude the activity. For others it may be of benefit to discuss the above lines of argument in **general terms**, thus working at Proof Level 3.

12. Algebra may be appropriate if this activity is undertaken with pupils in secondary school. The above explanations can be expressed algebraically, using r to represent the number of red lollipops, as $r + (r - 1)$, or $2(r - 1) + 1$, or $2r - 1$, the latter being the simplest form of the other two.

Pupils capable of understanding this may also be able to appreciate the equivalence of all these different approaches.

13. Partly because of the length of time needed to complete this activity, and partly because of the complexity of the explanations, written reports are unlikely to benefit many pupils in primary schools. A minority of primary pupils and some secondary pupils could write a report. It may describe and explain the pattern and connection for green lollipops, give one explanation for the total number of lollipops being an odd number, and possibly a calculation with reasons about the total for (say) fifty red lollipops. The report can either be written in retrospect, or at appropriate points in the discussion.

Pupil Challenge

Overlapping circles

  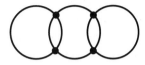

How many dots for lots of circles?

Look for patterns.
Try to describe them.
Can you explain them?

Convince a friend.

This activity is suitable for use in either primary or secondary schools. If pupils start with this activity it may provide their first experience in explaining the connections between a visual pattern and a simple number pattern. It may also be the first time they have met a numerical question without specific numbers. In order to deal with this pupils will use the problem-solving strategies of starting with the simplest case, and of tabulating data, and also gain practice in recognising number patterns. Expectations are slightly greater here in that the only practical work is drawing, and pupils begin working independently (possibly collaborating in pairs) earlier and for longer.

Lesson Outline (20 - 30 minutes)

Overlapping circles

1. Show pupils a row of overlapping circles on the board, or hand out worksheet.

2. Ask pupils for a sensible way of starting.

3. Instruct pupils to draw their own circles and count and record the number of dots.

4. Pupil volunteers draw diagrams and tabulate results on board.

5. Class discussion – ask pupils to describe any patterns.

   (Multiples of two – successive differences may be helpful.)

6. Invite pupils to suggest reasons for this. (Two dots for each new circle.)

   (Some pupils may write one sentence.)

7. In pairs or small groups, ask pupils to look for connections between the number of dots and number of circles:– $d = 2(c - 1)$ or $d = 2c - 2$ (but probably without use of algebra).

8. Class discussion about the connections.

9. Conclude the discussion – ask one or two pupils to summarise the investigation by describing precisely how and why the number of twos relates to the number of dots in overlapping circles. (Some pupils may write second sentence.)

(10. Algebra, if appropriate.)

Lesson Plan

1. At the beginning of the lesson **show pupils a line of overlapping circles**, probably on the board, and tell them that they are going to investigate the number of dots for different numbers of circles. Whether or not to give each pupil a copy of the pupil worksheet is left to the discretion of teacher.

   If this is pupils' first experience of answering an open-ended problem they may need reassurance that "lots" does not mean a specific large number.

2. **Ask pupils for a sensible way of starting** the investigation or remind them that a sensible way to start the investigation is to draw one circle, and count dots as new circles are added.

   Draw one circle on the board and ask pupils for the number of dots (none), which is recorded in a table as shown below.

Number of circles	Number of dots
1	0
2	2
3	4

Add a second circle and again record the number of dots suggested by pupils.

If pupils have previously engaged in problem-solving activities they can be expected to start the investigation confidently. If this is their first experience they need to start with a simple case and may need help in tabulating the results.

3. **Instruct pupils to draw their own circles**, freehand or round coins or counters, and to count and record number of dots as more circles are added.

Pupils may say that they know the pattern. As it is difficult to listen to them all individually they should be encouraged to try to write their ideas down. They may well find this difficult but should be encouraged to persist, perhaps as part of a letter to a friend describing the discovery they have made. They will not have long to write, as this part of the activity will only take a few minutes.

4. When all pupils have drawn at least five circles and recorded the numbers of dots **ask one pupil to come to the board to draw circles, and a second to continue the table by recording the numbers of dots**. Encourage other pupils to observe what they are doing and compare with their own results.

A few pupils will probably be prepared to come to the board. However if this is their first experience of this approach, and no-one volunteers it is strongly recommended that gentle persuasion be exercised in order to prevent this part of the lesson becoming a solo performance by the teacher, during which pupils may lose interest.

5. Begin **class discussion** by ensuring that all pupils have recorded correct values. Then **ask pupils** to describe any patterns they observe in the second column. Collect several responses by recording them on the board very briefly, eg. +2, even. Discourage pupils from writing these suggestions at this point. It may be considered helpful to highlight the usefulness of finding successive differences but this strategy should not be laboured nor formalised at this stage.

Expected responses at this point include:–
- the number of dots increases by two

or • the numbers are even

or • in the two times table

or • multiples of two

or • divisible by two.

6. **Invite pupils to suggest reason**s for this and again consider several responses. It may be necessary to ask some pupils by name for their ideas.

   Some pupils will be able to explain, in a variety of ways, that overlapping one circle over another circle creates two dots, and so adding each new circle increases the number of dots by two; or creates two lines of dots. It may be appropriate to ask some pupils to write a sentence, including the word "because", describing the pattern and then explaining it.

7. **Ask pupils to look for connections** relating the number of dots to the number of circles. It may be advisable to allow pupils to discuss their ideas **in pairs or small groups**. Some pupils may find this difficult as they do not naturally look for such connections.   Many are satisfied that they have solved the problem if they know how to continue the pattern, in this case by writing successive multiples of two.   If so it may be worthwhile drawing the attention of the class to the disadvantage of relying on this approach by asking pupils to consider how many dots for many (say) fifty circles.

   Able and/or confident pupils may find a connection that satisfies them very quickly.   They should be encouraged to write their ideas down while the teacher emphasises to other pupils the need to look for direct connections from the number of circles to the number of dots.   Some pupils may need explicit instruction to compare their results with the first few multiples of two, in the expectation that they will then observe the need to subtract two.

8. After a few minutes begin a **class discussion** by asking pupils for their suggestions **about the connections**. As these responses are more complex it may not be helpful to write them on the board, as some pupils may lose concentration while this is being done. Instead ensure, by repeating if necessary, that all pupils hear each suggestion, and encourage helpful comments. Pupils will have found a variety of ways of describing the connection

but essentially there are two equally valid methods.

i) Those whose thinking has been along the lines indicated above will suggest multiplying the number of circles by two, or doubling, and then subtracting two.

ii) Others will suggest that first they need to subtract one, and then multiply by two.

It may be appropriate to discuss the equivalence of these methods, but this should not be laboured.

9. To **conclude the discussion ask one or two pupils to summarise the investigation by describing precisely how and why the number of twos relates to the number of dots in overlapping circles.** Ask other pupils to add to these descriptions if they are incomplete. In classes where pupils wrote a sentence about the pattern of multiples of two they could be asked to add a second sentence which would complete their justification of the connection they observed. One or two of these pupils could then read out both the sentences they have written. At this point some pupils will be able to fully explain one of the above methods of relating the number of dots to the number of circles.

i) The number of dots is doubled because there are two for each new circle, but the first circle did not overlap to create any dots and so two must be subtracted.

ii) Only new circles add pairs of dots and so the first circle is not included in the number to be doubled.

10. In classes where pupils are familiar with elementary algebra variables may be defined to represent the number of circles, say c, and the number of dots, say d, and to derive and compare direct connections between explicit variables.

Pupils who are competent in their use of elementary algebra may relate "c" and "d" in several ways:–

i) $d = c \times 2 - 2$ or $d = 2c - 2$

ii) $d = (c - 1) \times 2$ or $d = 2(c - 1)$

While the first version in each pair should be praised for being correct the more sophisticated equivalents should be encouraged. However it is important that discussions about use of algebra do not detract from the main purpose of the activity, namely to establish that the observed patterns can be explained.

Pupil Challenge

Row of squares

How many matches in lots of squares?

Look for patterns.
Try to describe them.
Can you explain them?

Convince a friend.

This investigation analyses the number of line segments or matches required to form a row of squares, as shown above. Brown (1995, p37) proposes this pattern for initial experience in recognising and explaining number patterns as "pupils can be asked to produce a convincing statement of how it is generated, and then to justify a rule".

The aims here are essentially the same as those for the previous activity. However the resulting number pattern is less obvious, in that it requires pupils to appreciate a combination of two simple patterns simultaneously, and also there are several valid, apparently different but essentially similar, ways of explaining it.

Lesson Outline (about 30 minutes)

Row of squares

1. Draw a row of three squares on the board.
2. Consider one square and start a table.
3. Pupils continue.
4. Collate pupil results.
5. Remind pupils to find and explain pattern – pairs or small groups.
6. Class discussion of pupil suggestions, using words to describe patterns.
7. (7. Written reports if appropriate.)
8. (8. Algebraic analysis if appropriate.)

Lesson Plan

Because of its similarity to the first investigation this plan is less detailed at Stages 1 to 4 to avoid repetition.

1. **Draw a row of three squares on the board** and explain the task. Give out matches if they are needed. Again the use of individual pupil worksheets is optional.

2. **Consider one square.** Set up a table for collecting results as shown below:–

Number of squares	Number of matches
1	4
2	7
3	

3. **Pupils continue drawing** or making squares and recording results.

4. **Collate pupil results** on the board.

5. **Remind pupils that they need to find and then explain the number pattern**, or consider the structure of the visual pattern in order to identify the number pattern. Because the number pattern is not obvious, it is likely that some pupils will pursue the second course of action. It is not helpful in this investigation to separate the patterns. **Allow pupils a few minutes to discuss the results in pairs or in small groups**. If a significant number of pupils seem unable to make any progress it may be advisable to draw the attention of the class to the usefulness of examining successive differences. If only a small number of pupils have difficulty remind individuals of this approach. Those pupils who come to conclusions quickly should be asked to write their ideas down.

6. **Begin class discussion of results** when it seems that most pupils have formulated some ideas. Invite pupil volunteers to explain their thinking to the class, with an invitation to use the board if they wish. When volunteers have finished, encourage others to offer improvements or corrections if necessary, and in a non-critical manner. If several apparently different explanations are offered it is important to value all equally at this stage, in the hope that this will help to give pupils more confidence to contribute to discussions. If the first pupil contribution is correct and complete it will be necessary to explain to the class that

there are several ways of looking at the problem and to encourage further ideas.

Some pupils will realise that one has been added to multiples of three. Those who analyse the structure of the diagrams may observe the same connection, after realising that each new square adds three new matches, and the first square also needs an extra match. This, with two other possible analyses of the pattern, is shown below:–

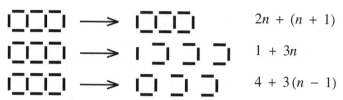

$$2n + (n + 1)$$

$$1 + 3n$$

$$4 + 3(n - 1)$$

7. Pupils who wrote sentences in the previous activity **should write their version of this pattern and its explanation.** Tell pupils that their report should include a full description of one number pattern, with a reason for each part/operation; or alternatively may begin with analysis of the visual pattern to obtain the number pattern. This task may be set for homework if there is not time in the lesson. If there is time in the lesson a few pupils could read out their report. This is less valuable if the report is written at home, as pupils need to be reminded of the previous lesson's work and the feelings of discovery are no longer present.

8. **Algebraic analysis** may be an appropriate extension for some pupils.

Algebraic expressions, using n for the number of matches, are included in the above diagram.

Pupils could represent the number of matches by m. Whether or not the equivalence of these is discussed depends on the competence of pupils to appreciate this, and also on the time available. The lesson should end with the emphasis on the fact that a pattern has been observed and explained – again the use of algebra should not detract from this.

Pupil Challenge

Reverse and add

1. Write down a two digit number, e.g. 62

2. Reverse the digits to form another two-digit number, e.g. 26

3. Add the two numbers, eg. 62
   $$\begin{array}{r} 62 \\ +\ 26 \\ \hline 88 \end{array}$$

4. Repeat for other two digit numbers.

5. What do you notice?

6. Can you explain why this happens?

Convince a friend.

The main purposes of this investigation are to encourage pupils to review the results of a repetitive process so that they learn to expect the presence of a relationship or pattern; and then to realise that such patterns can be explained. This activity may also provide revision and practice of addition of two-digit numbers, and division by eleven. The pupil worksheet illustrated above describes the essence of this investigation, but its use for individual pupils is optional.

Lesson Outline (about 30 minutes)

Reverse and add

1. Explain the task on the pupil worksheet.
2. Tell pupils to choose their own numbers and repeat the process.
3. Ask two or three pupils to write an addition on the board while the rest exchange books or use a calculator to check accuracy.
4. Tell pupils to work in pairs or small groups to examine their totals.
5. Begin class discussion with pupil suggestions and establish that totals are multiples of eleven; and possibly that they are multiples of the sum of the digits.
6. Ask pupils whether they think there is an explanation then ask for suggestions.

   Use narrowly focussed, questions about a particular case to establish the value of each digit, e.g.

$$62 + 26 = (6 + 2) \text{ tens} + (6 + 2)$$
$$= 8 \text{ tens } + 8$$
$$= 8 \times (10 + 1)$$
$$= 8 \times 11.$$

   i.e. for 62 + 26 there are eight tens and eight units which is equivalent to eight "ten-and-ones".

Lesson Plan

1. If pupils are to have their own printed instructions, hand out the pupil worksheets at the start of the lesson. Whether or not pupils have a worksheet, the problem should be **introduced by means of verbal explanations and a written example using a "vertical" layout,** developed on the board. It may be helpful to discuss a second example involving carrying figures, such as

$$\begin{array}{r} 58 \\ + \underline{85} \end{array}$$

2. Tell **pupils to choose their own numbers and repeat the process,** so that the results can be investigated. The decision as

to whether calculators should be allowed is left to the teacher. If banning calculators will not significantly affect pupil confidence, or impede progress in collecting results, this activity provides excellent practice in mental addition.

During this phase of the investigation it is assumed that pupils will be at the stage of benefiting from practice in adding two-digit numbers, but will have no major difficulties. If there are problems it is advisable to change the emphasis of the lesson at this point and defer the investigation of results.

3.   When pupils have done (say) five to eight additions, including at least two with carrying figures, **tell pupils to exchange books in order to check accuracy**. Calculators could be used for this. Meanwhile invite several **pupils to write one of their additions on the board** as examples.

4.   Tell **pupils to work in pairs or small groups to examine their totals** and those on the board, and to try to find what they all have in common. It may be necessary during this phase to advise either some groups or the whole class to separate their additions into two groups. In some cases it may be necessary to go further, and to direct pupils to treat additions with and without carrying figures separately. The length of time allowed for this part of the investigation will depend on the ability and interest of the pupils. Sufficient time can be allowed for weaker pupils. The more able, can be asked to consider how the number of elevens is related to the original numbers. Do **not** suggest that pupils investigate **three digit numbers** as these do not follow the same pattern.

Although the main objective here is to recognise the presence of multiples of eleven it is likely that pupils will also comment on the fact that the digit sum of each number is the same. Even though this seems trivial this should not be conveyed to pupils, but instead they should be asked to consider why this always happens, and what connection it has with the total. Pupils are likely to recognise that additions without carrying figures produce totals with two digits which are the same, and thence that they are multiples of eleven.   It is unlikely that pupils will recognise multiples of eleven and spontaneously consider testing for this in three digit answers.

5.   When most groups have developed their ideas, **begin class discussion of the results**. Invite **pupil suggestions** about the results of additions without carrying figures, and then consider

those with carrying figures. Discussion about the various ways of expressing the fact that the totals are multiples of eleven both reinforces this result, and also provides an opportunity to widen the mathematical vocabulary of pupils. It may be appropriate to ask some pupils to write down one version of the relationship.

The class discussion to establish that the totals are multiples of eleven is likely to be short, but may valuably be extended by considering alternative expressions, such as that totals are –

- in the eleven times table
- multiples of eleven
- divisible by eleven
- have a factor of eleven
- that eleven goes exactly into all totals.

The decision as to whether to extend the class discussion to consider the number of elevens in each case is left to the teacher.

6. It is interesting to **ask pupils** at this stage of learning about proof, **whether or not they think there is an explanation**. If they are reminded that they have repeated the same process each time they are likely to be receptive to the idea that an explanation exists, even if they did not appreciate this at first. Once it is established that there is likely to be an explanation **ask the class if any pupil has any suggestions as to why** all totals are multiples of eleven, or why the number of elevens is the sum of the digits in the original numbers, and discuss their responses. **Discussion in groups is unlikely to be productive** here as most pupils will not have spontaneous ideas, and will need prompting in order to elicit explanations. This is generally best achieved through individual (impractical) or class discussion, in this case by a generic example such as:–

$$\bullet \ 62 \ + \ 26 \ = \ (6 \ + \ 2) \text{ tens} + (6 \ + \ 2)$$

$$= \ 8 \text{ tens } + \ 8$$

$$= \ 8 \times (10 \ + \ 1)$$

$$= \ 8 \times 11.$$

Because of the likelihood that pupils will be unable to explain these results unaided it will be necessary for the teacher to use direct, **narrowly focussed, questions about a particular case** as a generic example. It will first be necessary to **establish the**

value of each digit in the example chosen, and then the "breakdown" of each number. In the example above the first number is made up of six tens and two units and the second is two tens and six ones (or units).

Addition of these gives **eight tens and eight units.** because addition is commutative, which can then be rearranged (physically using apparatus, diagrammatically, or mentally) as **eight "ten-and-ones" or eight elevens**. It may be necessary to discuss several examples of this type before pupils understand the general nature of the explanation. This can be verbalised as follows:– reversing and adding makes numbers with the same number of tens as ones; tens and ones can be paired to make elevens; and so the result must be a multiple of eleven. In discussion of the second type of example (58+85) it is necessary to replace the use of carrying figures by reference to the total as thirteen tens and thirteen ones and then proceed as above.

Some pupils may achieve only a superficial grasp of these explanations but it might be worth discussing them in order to reinforce the notion that an explanation exists.

7. Many pupils find it very difficult to write explanations of this property of numbers in their own words without considerable individual help. It is difficult to provide this help in a classroom while ensuring all pupils are on task. In such circumstances the teacher may decide that the advantages of having a written record are outweighed by the considerable practical difficulties.

Teachers may be tempted to ask pupils to copy an explanation from the board, but this is usually time-consuming and of limited value. Additionally the use of algebra to explain this property is unlikely to be accessible to all except the most able and is therefore not recommended here. The two main aims of this investigation can be achieved without detailed written explanations or use of algebra.

Pupil Challenge

Reverse and subtract

1. Write down a two digit number, e.g. 57

2. Reverse the digits to form another two-digit number, e.g. 75

3. Subtract the smaller number from the larger number.
    eg. Larger number   75
           Smaller number $- \underline{57}$
                                        18

4. Repeat for other two digit numbers.

5. What do you notice?

6. Can you explain why this happens?

Convince a friend.

The pupil worksheet above outlines this activity. Although the only apparent difference between this and the previous activity is that subtraction is used instead of addition, there are two other important structural differences. Pupils are less likely to recognise multiples of nine unless, perhaps, they have recently discussed the divisibility test as described earlier in this chapter; and neither diagrams nor apparatus are helpful. During the last phase of class discussion, about why the pattern occurs, it is important to remember that the emphasis is on learning about proof, rather than to prove. It will be necessary for the teacher to judge when to draw the discussion to a close, so that most pupils will realise that there is a reason and that some will understand the arguments, but that none are so bewildered that they lose the sense that there is a reason.

Despite these limitations the activity is appropriate at this stage because it provides an interesting context in which to practise subtraction; and because it provides a second example of a repetitive process producing a pattern which can be explained. However the teacher may defer this activity until pupils can recognise the results as a product of nine and the difference between the digits, and are sufficiently competent in their use of algebra to create their own proof.

Lesson Outline (about 30 minutes)
Reverse and subtract

1. Explain the task on the pupil worksheet. (It may be unwise to do subtraction on the board.)

2. Tell pupils to choose their own numbers and repeat the process.

3. Ask two or three pupils to write an addition on the board while the rest exchange books or use a calculator to check accuracy.

4. Tell pupils to work in pairs or small groups to examine their answers.

5. Begin class discussion with pupil suggestions if possible – order differences.

6. Use narrowly focussed, questions about a particular case, e.g.

$$75 - 57 = (7 - 5) \text{ tens} + (5 - 7)$$
$$= (7 - 5) \text{ tens} - (7 - 5)$$
$$= 2 \text{ tens} - 2$$
$$= 2 \times (10 - 1)$$
$$= 2 \times 9.$$

i.e. for $75 - 57$ there are two "ten-take-ones".

Lesson Plan

Because of the similarity to the previous activity this lesson plan is briefer and should be read in conjunction with the former. As before the pupil worksheet is optional.

1. When doing **an example of a subtraction on the board** it is unwise to utilise a particular method, except to set out in columns of tens and units, as it is likely that in any class several methods will be used but pupils may be confused by being shown a method unfamiliar to them.

   Instead **ask pupils to use their own methods and agree on an answer**. It may be advisable to do several examples together to ascertain whether pupils are able to subtract two-digit numbers unaided.

2-4. Proceed as in the previous activity except that is unnecessary to consider two types of subtractions. During the **group discussions about finding a pattern** many pupils may be unable to make progress unaided. The teacher may prefer to curtail group discussions and to begin class discussion sooner. Again it is not recommended that pupils consider three-digit subtractions as, although the result is the same, it is difficult to explain without using algebra.

5. As pupils are less likely to recognise multiples of nine, unless they have recently discussed the divisibility test for nine, it may be necessary to make direct suggestions such as **ordering all the differences**. Perhaps a pupil could be invited to write the numbers in a column on the board. Once **multiples of nine have been recognised the connection between the number of nines and the original numbers should be considered**. If pupils have done the previous activity in their recent past they may recognise this connection. However recording examples of pairs of digits producing each difference on the board may be needed before this happens.

6. Although pupils will be less surprised that an explanation exists, **group discussions are still not recommended** because pupils are unlikely to find these unaided. The **class discussion** will be similar to, but probably take longer than, that in the previous example.

   A suitable generic example for discussion is on the pupil worksheet:–

$$\bullet \ 75 \ - \ 57 \ = \ (7 \ - \ 5) \ \text{tens} + (5 \ - \ 7)$$
$$= \ (7 \ - \ 5) \ \text{tens} \ \ - \ (7 \ - \ 5)$$
$$= \ 2 \ \text{tens} \ \ - \ 2$$
$$= \ 2 \times (10 \ - \ 1)$$
$$= \ 2 \times 9.$$

It may be possible to establish that this is the same as two "ten-take-ones", which is the same as two nines but do not labour this as visual aids are not helpful and pupils are likely to find it difficult. Try to end the discussion on a positive note!

7.   Again, written reports and algebra are not recommended.

Pupil Challenge

Handshakes

At Pat's birthday party everyone shakes hands
with everyone else.

Investigate the number of handshakes.

Look for patterns.

Try to describe them.

Can you explain them.

Convince a friend.

Questions forming the basis of this investigation are frequently used to provide experience in problem-solving. In essence they ask pupils to find the number of handshakes involved when everyone in a room shakes hands with everyone else, and usually specify a number such as thirty, or fifty. Because, in the context of learning about proof, the notion of a general case needs to be conveyed, it is preferable that a number is not specified. For this reason the pupil worksheet does not include a particular number. Instead pupils should be encouraged to consider small numbers of people initially, and look for patterns in the results, and then for explanations.

This investigation provides pupils with experience of proof in a "practical" context, and can be used to demonstrate that apparently very different ways of explaining a pattern can both be correct and equally valid. Analysis of this problem involves adding consecutive integers from one. Pupils should have previously discussed this (earlier in this chapter). There are three points at which the investigation can be concluded, with the latter stages being included to extend more able, or highly motivated, groups of pupils.

Lesson Outline (20–50 minutes)
Handshakes

1. Explain the task.
2. Tell pupils to shake hands in small groups and tabulate results.
3. Complete table of results on board; use to describe patterns and predict.
4. Check by demonstrating with small group shaking hands systematically.
5. Begin class discussion about proof. Can pupils explain the addition of consecutive integers? (Possible, but not recommended, conclusion.)

    Continue discussion. Consider fifty people. Find alternative solution.

    e.g. Try $\times 2, 3, 4, \ldots$; $+ 2, 3, 4 \ldots$; $\times (n + 1), (n - 1)$; then $\div 2$.

6. Try to elicit pupil suggestion of need for proof. If none made ask directly for an explanation of "$\times (n - 1) \div 2$" (Everyone within group (n) shakes hands with everyone else ($n - 1$), but only one handshake between each pair counted ($\div 2$).) (Probable conclusion.)

    Could continue. Attempt to reconcile two approaches.
7. (Written reports if appropriate.)

Lesson Plan

1. **Explain the problem** to the class orally. A written copy with the open question, "How many handshakes are there?" may confuse some pupils, who might expect to be able to provide a single numerical answer to such a question. An oral explanation can emphasise the need to answer the question for several, initially small, numbers of people.

2. Tell pupils to **shake hands within small groups** of pupils near to them. They may need to be reminded of the usefulness of tabulating results. These are shown in the table below for up to six people in a group. Larger groups tend to create chaos in the classroom, and some teachers may feel that groups of four or five are large enough.

Number of people	Number of handshakes
1	0
2	1
3	3
4	6
5	10
6	15

Except for the practical nature of this task the outcomes will be similar to previous investigations.

3. Begin class discussion by **completing a table of results** on the board using pupil responses for the numbers of handshakes. Ask pupils to **describe any patterns** they observe. If their suggestions can be written very briefly, e.g. successive differences, list them or add them to the table if appropriate. At this stage it is not necessary to probe too deeply for further suggestions of patterns or for explanations. Use the pupil suggestions to **predict** the number of handshakes for the next number of people recorded.

The level of discussion at this stage will depend on whether or not pupils have previously added consecutive integers from one or been introduced to triangle numbers. The most likely point of discussion will be that the differences between successive terms increase by one. However, it is possible that, if triangle numbers are recognised, pupils may also recognise that they may be found by multiplying the number of people by one less, and halving the result. Unless this is suggested by a pupil defer discussing it at this stage.

4. To **check** the above prediction, select that number of pupils to form a group at the front of the class and **shake hands in a systematic way**, namely by introducing one pupil at a time into the group, so that the number of handshakes can be counted by others in the class. Repeat this for the next number of people if necessary, until pupils appreciate that the patterns they have suggested seem to be producing the correct values.

    Pupils are unlikely to experience difficulty in predicting the next number of handshakes. The apparent intention of organising a group of children to shake hands at the front of the class is to check the prediction. However, if the pupils are introduced into the group one by one it can also be used to demonstrate that "the previous number" is added each time, so helping pupils to understand the situation.

5. **Ask pupils** if they can now **explain why** the total number of handshakes is obtained by adding "the previous number". Invite several pupils to explain their thinking. It is possible to conclude the activity here but if the interest of the pupils is sufficiently high consideration of an alternative approach is recommended if at all feasible. Continue by raising the question of finding the number of **handshakes among (say) fifty** people. Some pupils will be happy to continue patterns down the table to find this, but can usually appreciate the advantage of using **relationships across the table.** Try to elicit these from pupils. It may be necessary to use direct questions, and to introduce an element of trial and error. Trials could include adding to the number of people, or multiplying by, first a constant, and then a number related in a simple way to the number of people. If necessary make direct suggestions for their consideration, until the equivalent of multiplying by $n - 1$ and dividing by two has been obtained.

    Pupils may be able to explain that as each new member is introduced into the group (s)he shakes hands with all the rest, thus adding the size of the group prior to this last person, but in some classes prompting to elicit the necessary detail may be necessary. It is possible that a pupil may observe how to calculate the number of handshakes from the number of people, but more likely that "guided trial and improvement" may be necessary. If so, first ask pupils for useful suggestions about what operation they could apply to the number of people to obtain the number of handshakes for different numbers of people.

6. When pupils have found an **alternative way** of finding the number of handshakes **raise the question of how can they be sure this is correct**, bearing in mind it will be impractical to perform the experiment. Attempt to elicit from pupils the suggestion that they need to explain why the pattern works. If this is not possible it may be necessary to **ask directly why** it should. Follow up any correct response or clarify any misunderstandings, until pupils seem to appreciate an explanation. It is possible to conclude the discussions at this point but, if pupil interest can be maintained, it is preferable if the **two different approaches can be reconciled**. An effective way of doing this at this level is indicated in the diagrams below. These are similar to, but not the same as, the diagrams for adding consecutive integers from one. In this case it is necessary to include zero as the first person does not shake hands. For most pupils an algebraic analysis is not recommended.

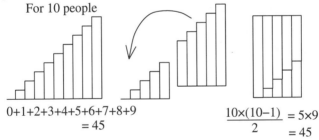

For 10 people

$$0+1+2+3+4+5+6+7+8+9$$
$$= 45$$

$$\frac{10 \times (10-1)}{2} = 5 \times 9$$
$$= 45$$

Pupils are unlikely to be able to explain this result. The teacher will have to show that the pattern observed is valid because every person shakes hands with every other, so justifying the product "number of people × (number of people − 1)". However, this involves counting each handshake twice and so it is therefore necessary to divide this product by two. If an attempt is made to reconcile the two different approaches to this problem, some pupils may be able to interpret the diagram and explain it to the class.

7. Although this is a lengthy investigation, those pupils who have become accustomed to writing explanations should **write a**

short report about solving the problem. They will need **clear guidance** about what is expected of them. A recommendation is that they include a description of the problem, a table of results, a description of at least one pattern, and its explanation. They are unlikely to be able to explain the connection between the approaches in their own words. For pupils of above average ability in writing skills, a more realistic expectation is that they should **describe the problem, tabulate results, and describe two ways of solving the problem**. The written reports of all pupils could be usefully enhanced by a copy of the above diagrams, or they could be used as an alternative to written explanations for weaker pupils. Not all pupils who are able to understand the explanations will also be able to write about them. In such cases teachers may decide not to pursue this. Their pupils will still have gained valuable experience during this investigation.

Writing about this type of mathematics is difficult for many pupils and a full report should only be undertaken by pupils whose writing skills are considered to be above average.

Pupil Challenge

A new team strip

The pupils in the school rounders team are
choosing a new team strip.

They are choosing from five
colours – blue, green, red,
yellow, and white.

They are to choose any three
different colours.

How many different sets are
there?

How can you be sure you have found all possible sets?

Convince a friend.

This example of a proof by exhaustion is essentially an
investigation to find the number of ways of choosing three out of five
(ten ways). This context is a practical activity suitable for pupils in
primary schools.

Lesson Outline (30 minutes)

A new team strip

1. Explain task.
2. Ask pupils to suggest ways of starting.
3. Discuss the importance of being systematic.
4. Tell pupils to work in pairs or small groups, and provide materials.
5. When some appear to have finished ask them for results.
6. Tell pupils to continue looking and considering the justification for their maximum number.
7. Pupil volunteers announce their totals and convince the class. Other pupils comment. End the discussion with correct solution (10 sets) and explanation and reference to proof by exhaustion.
8. Poster showing all possible sets. (Some may add sentence to explain.)

Lesson Plan

1. **Explain the task**, and possibly show pupils samples of fabric in (any) five colours so that a few pupils can make their selection of three colours. The pupil worksheet is not important, especially for pupils who may find reading difficult.

2. Ask **pupils to suggest ways of starting** the investigation. Try to elicit ideas about what they can use to help them.

    These should include coloured pencils, paints, coloured paper, counters or cubes. Pupils could either be given a free choice or provided with materials. If they use counters or cubes they can either be given access to a large supply or told to record selections on paper.

3. Before they are allowed to begin practical work **discuss the importance of being systematic**. Remind them that they will have to be sure they have found all combinations if they are to convince someone else.

4. Tell **pupils to work in pairs or small groups** and encourage them to discuss their strategy before they start. They will then need to collect or be given the **materials** they are going to use. It may be appropriate to encourage pupils in some classes to make posters showing their results.

5.   Allow sufficient **time for some pupils to find as many sets as they can.** Then ask some of them how many they have found.

     Pupils are unlikely to agree that the maximum number is ten, but try not to indicate that this is the expected number.

6.   **Tell pupils to continue** looking for different sets of three colours **and to discuss** with each other the **justification for their maximum number**.

     Pupils who finish early could be asked to consider other logical orders for their choices to see if they can improve their work.

7.   Stop group work when when most pupils are satisfied they have found all possible combinations of colours, and think they could convince someone else of this. Ask for **pupil volunteers to announce their totals and to try to convince the class** that they have found all combinations. Ask **other pupils to comment** on the explanations. If possible try to **end the discussion with the identification of the ten sets of colours** in a logical order so that it is possible to justify that none have been omitted.

     When pupils volunteer responses they might prefer to to do so in pairs so that one can display the results while the other explains their thinking.

8.   If a record is required on paper the poster referred to above (at Stage 4) may be sufficient. Some teachers may wish pupils to write a sentence to the effect that they are sure the total is ten because they have listed all possible sets in a logical order, and so none have been omitted. However this is not an essential part of this activity.

This investigation can be continued in a non-mathematical way by asking pupils to use their favourite set of three colours to design a new team strip. Most pupils will enjoy this, and linking mathematics to pleasurable activities whenever possible is strongly recommended.

An alternative context for choosing three out of five, suitable for older pupils, is joining dots to form triangles in "Dot-to-dot Triangles".

Pupil Challenge

Dot-to-dot triangles

• *A*

• *B*   • *C*

• *D*   • *E*

Draw a set of five labelled dots.

Do not copy this set, but make sure you don't choose three dots in a straight line.

Make several copies of your set of dots.

On each set draw a triangle by joining any three dots.

How many different triangles can you draw?

How can you be sure you have found all possible triangles?

Convince a friend.

Although this lesson is described in a similar way to previous proof activities some teachers may prefer the alternative strategy of introducing and explaining the task near the end of a lesson and asking pupils to continue the investigation for homework, in preparation for sharing ideas in the next lesson. This approach has been used with thirteen year old pupils of average ability.

Lesson Outline (20–30 minutes)

Dot-to-dot triangles

1. Draw five dots on the board and label them.
2. Explain task. Raise need to work systematically and explain need for several copies of sets of dots.
3. Tell pupils draw their own dots.
4. Tell pupils draw three or four triangles and think about possible difficulties.
5. Discuss possible difficulties. Discuss strategies of labelling and listing.

6. Tell pupils to draw as many different triangles as they can. After a few minutes ask some pupils their totals.
7. Tell pupils to continue collecting results and thinking about justifying total.
8. Ask for pupil volunteers to announce their total and convince the class it is correct. Ask other pupils to comment. Conclude discussion with correct solution and explanation and reference to proof by exhaustion.
(9. Written reports if appropriate.)

Lesson Plan

1. The use of pupil worksheets is again optional. **Draw** an array of **five dots**, no three collinear, **on the board and label** each, say A, B, C, D, E. Emphasise the importance of the array not including three dots forming a straight line.

2. **Explain the task** and ask pupils how they intend to start. Try to elicit suggestions about the importance of **working in an organised and systematic way**. If it is not suggested by a pupil highlight the problems caused by drawing overlapping triangles, and **explain the need for** several identical copies of a set of dots.

   Difficulties incurred by overlapping triangles include errors in counting, extra triangles formed by overlap, and difficulties in reviewing what has been done in order to justify a claim.

3. Decide whether pupils should work individually or in pairs to collect results. Ask **pupils to draw their own array of dots** on paper, and to make several identical copies, or provide them with more than ten copies of an appropriate array. However it is preferable that they create their own arrays as this incorporates a degree of generality rather than uniformity.

4. **Tell pupils to draw three or four different triangles, and then to think** about possible difficulties in drawing, counting, and being sure about the total.

5. **Ask pupils** for their thoughts **about possible difficulties** and discuss how they might be overcome. Try to elicit from pupils the usefulness of **labelling the dots and of listing** triangles by sets of three letters. Again emphasise the advantages of being systematic, but do not give the pupils a list of triangles to draw.

6. Tell **pupils to draw as many different triangles as they can find** and remind them that they have to be able to explain how they can be sure they have found them all. When some pupils think they have found them all **ask several pupils how many** they have found.

   It is unlikely that all pupils will agree that the maximum number is ten, but try not to indicate that this is the expected number.

7. **Tell pupils to continue their investigation and to discuss** with each other the **justification for their maximum number**. If pupils have been working individually they could benefit at this stage by sharing results and ideas with a partner. Those pupils who finish early should try to write their explanations down.

   It is possible that a few pupils may still need help with drawing, counting and recording triangles.

8. When about half of the pupils are satisfied they have found all triangles and think they could convince someone else of this ask for **pupil volunteers to announce their totals and to try to convince the class** that they have found all triangles. If appropriate encourage them to use the board for drawing or listing triangles. Ask **other pupils to comment** on the explanations. If possible try to **end the discussion with a list of ten sets of three letters**, to represent triangles, in a logical order so that it is possible to justify that none have been omitted. Finally explain to pupils that this has created a **"proof by exhaustion"** (A proof method, not a description of pupils and teacher at the end of this activity!), which may only take about twenty minutes.

   When pupils volunteer responses they might prefer to to do so in pairs so that one can use the board while the other explains their thinking.

9. If a report is needed it could include the triangles already drawn, an ordered list of sets of vertices, and a sentence about why pupils are sure there are exactly ten triangles.

   A similar investigation, appropriate for younger pupils, is to consider the number of ways of arranging three objects (six ways), say give three different toys to three children (one each). Older pupils could choose four out of six (fifteen ways), say people for goes on a go-cart, or find four digit numbers from six digits.

"Not Proofs"

In this informal treatment of proof it is not helpful to attempt to define what proof is, but it is worthwhile to try to distinguish between what is and what is not proof. This section includes explanations which look like proofs but which are not proofs. The following examples point towards the rigour associated with formal proof, but it is recognised that for some pupils consideration of these may create insecurity in their understanding of numbers, and may therefore be ill-advised during this phase.

Number

Multiplication of directed numbers

One way of introducing this topic is to consider multiplication tables "backwards". Thus

$3 \times 3 = 9$	Commutativity then gives	$-3 \times 3 = -9$
$3 \times 2 = 6$	Continuing this pattern gives	$-3 \times 2 = -6$
$3 \times 1 = 3$		$-3 \times 1 = -3$
$3 \times 0 = 0$		$-3 \times 0 = 0$
$3 \times -1 = -3$		$-3 \times -1 = 3$
$3 \times -2 = -6$		$-3 \times -2 = 6$
$3 \times -3 = -9$		$-3 \times -3 = 9$

Whilst this is an excellent explanation it is not proof in the sense that it is impossible to consider all cases in this way.

Recurring decimals

During this phase pupils are likely to encounter the fact that $^1/_3 = 0.3333..........= 0 \cdot \dot{3}$, and thence that $^2/_3 = 0.6666.......= 0 \cdot \dot{6}$. It may be appropriate to consider the value of $^3/_3$. Continuing the pattern would seem to suggest that this is $0.9999..... = 0 \cdot \dot{9}$, but pupils already know, $^3/_3 = 1$! Continuing a pattern has produced a surprising result, but has not proved that it is true. A formal proof is not appropriate at this stage, but this property of numbers is included here because some pupils are fascinated by ideas of infinity. The possible equality of $0 \cdot \dot{9}$ and 1 is discussed again in Chapter 4, where formal proofs are compared.

Adding "half"

This is similar to the previous example in that it involves consideration of what happens at infinity. In the following series what is the total if the fractions continue for ever?

$$1 + \frac{1}{2} + \frac{1}{4} + \frac{1}{8} + \frac{1}{16} + \frac{1}{32} + \frac{1}{64} + \ldots$$

Pupils can construct a diagram showing successive halves of, say, a square:–

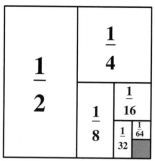

This suggests that the outcome at infinity will be 1 but it is not a proof that it will happen.

Paradoxes

During this phase the danger of making assumptions about whether claims are true or false without proof and, by implication, the need for proof, can be powerfully illustrated by the consideration of some simple paradoxes. The following three, from "Riddles in Mathematics" (Northrop, 1961, but originally 1944, p11) are suitable examples. Northrop describes a paradox as "anything which offhand appears to be false, but is actually true; or which appears to be true, but is actually false; or which is simply self-contradictory."

True or false?

1. Two men and two sons leave town. The population is reduced by three. True or false?

   The statement is true because the group includes grandfather, father, and son.

2. A man says "I am lying."

   Is his statement true? If so, then he is lying and the statement is false.

Is his statement false? If so, then he is lying and the statement is true.

3. Volumes 1, 2, and 3, of a series of books are each two centimetres thick and are placed on a bookshelf in numerical order, from left to right.

A bookworm starts at the outside front cover of Volume 1 and eats its way to the outside back cover of Volume 3. It travels six centimetres. True or false? (Obviously it actually travels only through Volume 2, i.e. two centimetres.)

This serves as an excellent warning against making hasty judgements, or neglecting reasoned argument.

Sharing camels

The paradox about sharing 35 camels between three brothers so that the first has one half, another has one third, and the last has one ninth of the camels is set in an entertaining context in "The Man Who Counted" (Tahan, translated by Clark and Reid, 1994, pp 11-13). The solution by borrowing a camel which is later returned to its owner results in an additional unclaimed camel. This extra camel can be explained by the fact that the original three fractions do not add to one and so the problem could not be solved exactly as apparently intended. This example serves to illustrate the value of checking that a problem has a solution.

Optional Assessment Task

In the opinion of the author there is little value at this stage of formal assessment of ability to prove. For many pupils formal assessment at this stage will be impractical because of limited ability to express thought processes in writing, and limited feasibility in most classrooms to effect individual or small group interviews. For those cases when informal assessment is desirable or viable the following investigation based on a row of triangles is suggested. This does not, nor cannot, involve only proof. Teachers may select some or all of the following as appropriate aims:–

- to provide an opportunity for pupils to find and explain patterns independently;
- to provide details about strengths and weaknesses in pupils' abilities to obtain and record data, to search for patterns, and to explain them;
- to provide evidence of level of understanding about proof.

Pupil Challenge

Row of triangles

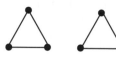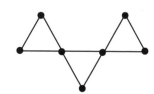

How many dots and matches for lots of triangles?

Look for patterns.
Try to describe them.
Can you explain them?

Convince a friend.

The diagram involves two patterns, namely the number of sides (or "matches") and the number of dots. Whether one or both are investigated is left to the teacher to decide. Although the task should be explained orally to the pupils, it may be helpful for some pupils to have copies of the first few stages of the pattern, so that they may count dots and/or matches more easily. The numbers of matches are likely to be recognised as multiples of three and these explained by reference to triangles having three sides. The numbers of dots are likely to be recognised as odd numbers, and may either be perceived as the first dot with two for every triangle $(1 + 2n)$, or three for the first triangle with two more for each additional triangle $(3 + 2(n - 1))$.

Pupils could be instructed to investigate individually to obtain results, identify patterns, and explain them; or alternatively the results and possible patterns could be derived via class discussion and pupils only required to write explanations for assessment. If the former approach is adopted then skills, additional to proving, form a substantial part of the assessment. In the second approach the teacher must be aware that inability to write a proof does not necessarily imply an inability to prove.

The way in which the test is marked depends on the aim(s) of the assessment selected by the teacher. If it is to provide pupils with the opportunity for independent exploration and reporting of findings, then formative assessment of individual attainment through helpful comments on errors and omissions, and congratulatory comments for correct responses are sufficient. If comparison between pupils or a summative assessment is required, then it will be necessary to produce relative measures. Whereas the problem-solving element of the test, namely, finding the patterns, might be criterion-referenced, with marks allocated for collation of results and derivation and description of patterns, this is not appropriate for the proof element. Reference to the descriptors of the Proof Levels provides a relative measure only if it is assumed that no pupil is handicapped by difficulties in writing proof. Thus an assessment of this type can only provide a valid indicator of ability to prove for certain pupils.

Conclusion

By the end of this phase most pupils will at least have an awareness of proof, albeit in terms of systematic checking (Proof Level 2), and some will understand the need for a generalised proof (Proof Level 3). With guidance, some able pupils may produce simple written proofs (approaching Proof Level 4).

The time scale for achieving these Proof Levels is deliberately not specified. It will depend on the amount of time teachers consider they can devote to this aspect of mathematics, while still maintaining satisfactory progress in other aspects. This in turn will depend on factors like total time available for lessons and homeworks, and age, ability and interest of pupils. Whilst highly motivated, very able twelve year old pupils, or average ability sixteen year old pupils might attain Level 3 in a few months, others will take more than one year.

Once pupils are aware of the need for proof they can reasonably be expected to benefit from continued use of proof in the classroom, and more investigations producing patterns requiring explanations. Both of these are described in the next chapter.

CHAPTER 3

Phase 2 – Teaching and learning to prove

*Pupils realise that, except for a few accepted truths
(axioms), all mathematical statements can be subjected
to proof which is independent of particular cases. Proof
discussions are therefore more substantial in this
second phase. As pupils attempt to explain the results of
Proof Activities they begin to write short chains of
deductive reasoning, as they are challenged to –*

"Convince a penfriend!"

Introduction

The primary objectives during this phase are that pupils should
develop a firm grasp of the generalised nature of proof (Proof Level
3); and that they learn to write simple, but generalised, proofs (Proof
Level 4) independently if possible. Discussions about proving
mathematical statements and also results of Proof Activities should
become an integral part of the mathematical experiences of pupils,
and not just isolated, occasional incidents in the classroom. In such a
questioning environment pupils should adopt a questioning attitude to
mathematics, and also develop a willingness to search for their own
answers.

The programme of study described below is divided into three
sections. The first provides guidance about explaining mathematics
through Proof Discussions. The second describes Proof Activities
which are investigations, mainly leading to patterns, followed by
explanation of the results. By this stage both teachers and pupils
should be familiar with the idea of explaining all mathematical
statements, and the results of investigations. Teachers should no
longer require detailed instructions for each lesson. Therefore these
are not described in the same "step-by-step" way as in Chapter 2.
Instead some lessons with able pupils aged thirteen to sixteen, some
written pupil reports and some test and interview responses, are
described in detail. The twenty-five pupils involved in most lessons
were those referred to earlier as the experimental group. The last
section includes examples of "Not Proofs" in order to clarify further

the essence of what proof is. Teachers should select a blend of material from all three sections.

Finally an optional assessment task is provided for those pupils whose ability to prove in mathematics is not hindered by difficulties in writing.

Proof Discussions

Although pupils are no longer surprised by the idea that all mathematics can and should be proved or explained, they are still unable to do this unaided in the context of formal mathematics, and may need reminders that they should expect to be given reasons for all mathematical facts and properties. There will be a few occasions where proof is not feasible, because the mathematics involved is beyond pupils' current level of understanding. This should be admitted to pupils, and the difference between proof and demonstration highlighted. Some of these discussions are likely to be more substantial than during the previous stage, and possibly take place over several lessons. For this reason three of them are also summarised.

Number

In this section the first number property can be explained in words, diagrams and/or algebra but the second requires use of algebra and may therefore not be suitable for all pupils.

Multiplying odd and even numbers

Pupils are likely to be familiar with the results of multiplying odd and even numbers but not with explanations of the results. When asked to consider these some pupils may be able to offer explanations concerning even numbers but find the product of two odd numbers more difficult. The former are likely to be explained in terms of even numbers being perceived as "pairs" and any number of "pairs" being even. There are several lengthier explanations for the product of two odd numbers, two of which are indicated in the diagrams and statements below for "7 × 5":

** ** ** *	Odd × even = even	****** *	Even × even = even
** ** ** *		****** *	$6 \times 4 = 24$
** ** ** *	$7 \times 4 = 28$	****** *	Even + even = even
** ** ** *		****** *	$24 + 4 = 28$

| ** ** ** * | Even + odd = odd | ** ** ** * | Even + even + 1 = odd |
| | $28 + 7 = 35$ | | $28 + 6 + 1 = 35$ |

An algebraic approach is suitable for those who can express an even number as $2n$ and an odd number as $2n - 1$, and can also multiply binomials so that they can find and analyse $(2n - 1)(2m - 1)$.

Divisibility tests — algebraic approach

The algebraic analysis of the divisibility test for nine was discussed with some very able sixteen year old pupils in individual interviews, which are described in Chapter 5. These pupils did not find the proof easy. This might suggest that algebraic analysis is not appropriate during this phase. However those interviewed had little or no experience in proof and were initially given no guidance about how to proceed. For pupils familiar with the notions of proof and class discussions about proofs, the divisibility tests are appropriate during this phase.

Class discussion will begin by ensuring that all pupils are aware of the fact that the digit sum for multiples of nine is also a multiple of nine for two and possibly three-digit multiples. Pupils will also need to realise that this proof must be applicable to all such numbers. They should be asked for an appropriate representation of them. Hopefully they will suggest $10a + b$, and $100a + 10b + c$. Pupils might suggest these can be rewritten as $9a + a + b$ and $99a + 9b + (a + b + c)$. However these may only come after direct questions from the teacher such as, "If $a + b$ is removed from $10a + b$ what is left?" Once pupils have discussed and understood the test for two-digit numbers it is reasonable to expect some to be able to begin a proof for three-digit numbers. However they may still need guidance to complete this, and it is therefore best done orally.

Algebra

Although none of the proof activities during this phase depend entirely on the use of algebra for completion of a satisfactory proof, most use the language of algebra to express relationships after they have been explained in words. Here are two basic algebraic relationships which lend themselves to a diagrammatic approach, namely the product of some binomials as shown below.

Multiplying binomials

While the expansion of $(x + y)^2$, shown in Diagram 1, is likely to be accessible in this form to many pupils, a similar diagram for $(x - y)^2$ is less helpful because of the difficulty of illustrating $-y$. For the same reason the expansion of $(x - y)(x + y)$ is not attempted, but instead its converse, the factorisation of the difference of two squares, is readily illustrated in Diagrams 2.

Diagram 1

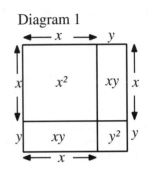

Diagrams 2

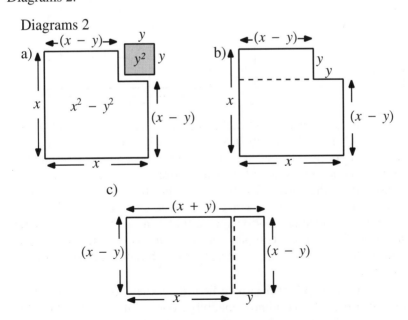

Area and Volume

Areas of rectilinear figures

The first lesson with the able fourteen and fifteen year old pupils who formed the experimental group and who had virtually no previous experience in proof was mainly a class discussion taking about thirty minutes, of familiar formulae for the area of a rectangle, a parallelogram, a triangle and a trapezium.

When asked why the area of a rectangle should be "length × breadth" their reactions were, predictably, that it was so because the formula always "worked". Further probing, using integer lengths (5cm and 3cm), elicited the correct response that using tiles of area 1cm² gave five rows of three and so justified multiplying the measures to find the area. This was readily accepted by the class but, as expected, they could not immediately explain why the same method also applied to a rectangle 5.4cm by 3.1cm. One pupil suggested that it was the same as before with an extra small rectangle, but he and the rest of the class readily perceived the error in this, when the following diagrams were drawn on the board.

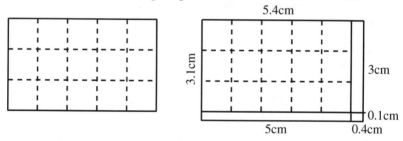

Closer examination of the rectangles that had been forgotten (5cm × 0.1cm and 3cm by 0.4cm) eventually led to the suggestion that the units be changed to millimetres. The argument could then proceed as before using tiles of area 1mm² and conversion to cm² demonstrated the correctness of the familiar formula in this instance. Some of the pupils were aware of the existence of even smaller units so the idea of further sub-division could be raised but not considered in detail. This is not a complete proof, which is beyond these pupils' understanding, but it is preferable to a blind acceptance of the formula.

When the pupils were asked how they knew the formula for the area of a triangle the almost inaudible comment was "Because Mr. … said so". This provided the opportunity to reinforce pupils' awareness that mathematical statements by teachers could, and should, be questioned. They should also attempt to answer the questions they raise for themselves.

Formulae for the areas of parallelograms, triangles and trapezia were deduced from that for a rectangle through class discussion aided by diagrams on the board, including contributions from pupils. For example, when asked to explain the formula for the area of triangle one pupil said that a triangle was half a rectangle and another that a rectangle could be made into two triangles. Part of the diagram below was drawn on the board and the pupils asked to explain this more fully. A girl tried to explain in words but found the verbal explanation difficult. She accepted the invitation to use the board and added a perpendicular height and arrows to complete the diagram shown below.

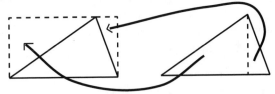

A parallelogram was perceived as two identical triangles and also as a dissected rectangle; and a trapezium as a rectangle and two triangles, a parallelogram and a triangle, or two triangles, this latter leading to the formula for area.

The direction of this discussion with older pupils who had little past experience of justifying mathematical claims, was dictated by their responses to a request for any formulae for area that they could remember. Ideally, areas of rectilinear figures would be introduced and explained through practical work and logical deduction over a period of several years. A recommended order for the introduction of these formulae is summarised as follows:–

- discover 'Area = length × breadth (or width)' for a rectangle with integer dimensions;
- discuss reasons for this result based on rows and columns of square units;
- consider the effect of non-integer dimensions;
- practical dissections of parallelograms to form rectangles leading to ...

- discussion to establish equality of these areas if base and height are equal, and thence
  Area = base × perpendicular height for a parallelogram;
- creation of parallelograms from two identical triangles leading to ...
- discussion to establish Area = ½ base × perpendicular height for a triangle and ...
- realisation that three different parallelograms are possible from two triangles and that therefore any side can be a base;
- dissection of trapezium into two triangles and thence that Area = ½ (sum of parallel sides) × perpendicular height.

This order is considered preferable to perceiving a triangle as half a rectangle, and then a parallelogram as two triangles because, coincidentally with the formula for the area of a triangle, it introduces the notion that any side can be a base.

Circumference and area of circles

Pupils should be allowed to measure the circumference and diameter for several circular objects and a set of results tabulated on the board. The ability and experience of the pupils will dictate whether it is agreed that the circumference is a little more than three times the diameter, or whether the class can adopt the more sophisticated approach of drawing a graph (hopefully a straight line with gradient near to 3.14) to demonstrate the constancy of the ratio "circumference : diameter". Pupils will be told that this ratio is the mathematical definition of π and that this is an accepted mathematical fact (or axiom) which does not have to be proved.

The formula for the area of a circle should, however, be deduced using a modification of the definition above, namely $C = 2\pi r$. Teachers will be familiar with the standard approach to this to dissect a circle into sixteen sectors and rearrange them to form a parallelogram (or rectangle).

Pupils should be encouraged to find their own re-arrangement. Some other possibilities are:–

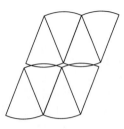 

| Taller, narrower parallelogram or rectangle | Triangle (if the number of pieces is square: 16, 36) |

Whichever methods of dissection are used the formula $A = \pi r^2$ should be deduced through class discussion of the dimensions, in terms of the radius and circumference, combined with relevant area formula for the selected shape(s). Some classes may be asked to consider the inaccuracies in all methods of dissection, and how they might be improved. This might then lead to a realisation that the result is only fully proved if there are infinitely many sectors each with an infinitely small angle and an infinitely small straight side. A helpful alternative approach to this is illustrated in "Images of Infinity" (Hemmings and Tahta, 1995, p 35). It shows "circles" formed from spirals of thick and thin string which are then cut into pieces of varying length to form approximate triangles.

Volume of cuboids and prisms

A class discussion with pupils in the experimental group began by asking them to explain why the familiar formula for finding the volume of a cuboid worked. They were able to do this in similar terms to those used when discussing area, namely using rows, columns and layers of unit cubes. Some could also justify it when the dimensions were not whole numbers. Although the pupils were familiar with the formula for the volume of a triangular prism, they had not previously considered why it was correct. They had, in Year 7, fitted together two congruent triangles, one of which was dissected along an altitude, to form a rectangle and were now able to extend the idea into three dimensions to establish why the volume of a triangular prism was half that of a cuboid with equal dimensions. Similar further discussion extended their knowledge of the area of a circle to three dimensions and an appreciation that a cylinder could be seen as a circular prism and thus the formula for its volume explained. Consideration of these three examples of prisms led to general agreement that the volume of a prism was $A \times l$. The lesson continued with practice exercises.

Geometry

Congruent triangles

The conditions for congruence can best be explained in terms of transformational reasoning (Simon, 1996) for secondary school pupils. While such a proof may be appreciated by pupils during this phase, some GCSE syllabi only require knowledge of the conditions for congruent triangles at higher levels of entry, and proof of mathematics about which pupils will not be examined may be afforded a low priority during this phase. Thus, although it is included in this section, this topic may be deferred to the next phase.

One commonly used approach to establishing the conditions for congruence of triangles is to ask each pupil in a class to draw triangles with specified measurements satisfying the conditions for congruence, and then observe that all pupils have drawn identical triangles. This serves only to demonstrate that the conditions apply to a particular case and does not constitute a generalised proof. The lesson described below involved a class discussion with pupils in the experimental group. The approach used is based on transformational reasoning in the belief that this promotes "the sense of understanding how it works" (Simon, 1996). It is not a formal rigorous proof but it is satisfactory in the context of raising pupil awareness of the nature of proof in that it illustrates the essential difference between demonstration and proof. Whilst this may not be proof in a formal sense it satisfies the definition suggested by Porteous (1994) and quoted in Chapter 1.

Instead of using drawings, triangles were formed from wooden rods, provided by the Technology Department. They were sorted into equal pairs of lengths 30cm, 40cm, 50cm, 60cm, 70cm, and 80cm. Also some sectors with angles 20°, 30°, 35°, and 60° were cut from stiff card. The rods and cards were colour coded so that triangles like those below could be formed.

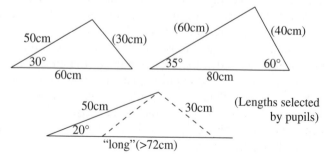

At the beginning of the lesson congruent shapes were defined as identical and examples were drawn on the board. It was suggested that although triangles had three angles and three sides it may be possible to establish congruence without knowing all six measures. It was generally agreed that pairs of triangles in which one or two sides and/or angles matched were not necessarily congruent, but that three matching sides and/or angles may be sufficient.

The pupils were shown the rods and invited to help make triangles. There was an enthusiastic response. Two pairs of pupils were each given an identical set of three rods. When the triangles formed were shown to the class (two pairs of hands were needed for this) it was agreed that they were "probably" – a word used emphatically by a pupil – identical. Then it was explained, and demonstrated, that although the first two sides could be laid down at any angle, fitting in the third side fixed the angle between them and also the the other two angles. The pupils accepted that, given three sides, only one triangle is possible.

Two new pairs of volunteers were then each given an identical set of two rods and a card angle to lay out, with the card between the rods, and asked to select the third rod to complete the triangle. The rest of the class agreed that, as they had chosen equal rods, they had made identical triangles. They clearly appreciated that, given two sides and the included angle, there was only one possible choice of third side, which had to join the free end points of two fixed sides.

The likelihood that a given side and two given angles would fix a triangle was considered and most pupils thought it likely. Two equal rods were shown to the class and one given to each pair of new volunteers. They were also given two angles in the same way and invited to choose two rods to complete a triangle. The rods they chose were compared to demonstrate that they were the same and the class agreed that the triangles were therefore congruent. They seemed to appreciate the explanation that fixing the base and base angles fixed the position of the other two sides and hence their point of intersection. They were then asked to consider the possibility that one of the two given angles was not a base angle. Several pupils were immediately able to explain that fixing two angles fixed the third and so the situation reduces to that described above.

The class was then shown two rods, one of fixed length and the other "long" (to represent unfixed length but fixed direction), at a fixed (card) angle to the first, and also a third rod of fixed length (i.e.

a two sides and a non-included angle) and asked whether or not only one triangle could be formed. Those who voiced an opinion thought that only one triangle was possible but readily appreciated that there were in fact two when they were shown to them. Then the special case of this ambiguous situation, with the given angle a right-angle, was considered. It was generally felt that only one triangle was possible but no-one could explain this spontaneously. One pupil pointing to the "unfixed" side said, "Because that side goes straight up." Another said that the other two angles were fixed because one angle was a right-angle. Other wild guesses without conviction followed. They were then asked what they knew about right-angled triangles and immediately Pythagoras' theorem was suggested. They then readily understood that if two sides of a right-angled triangle are given the third is also fixed and thus the situation reduces to being given three sides.

The class was then shown two rods at a fixed angle and a third placed in several parallel positions to create equiangular triangles to demonstrate that this is not a sufficient condition for congruence.

A summary of the conditions for congruent triangles, with appropriate diagrams, was written on the board for copying. The first two who finished, just before the end of the lesson, were invited to make quadrilaterals from identical sets of four rods. Not surprisingly they made different shapes but neither they nor anyone else in the class could explain why this was possible. When it was explained that quadrilaterals, unlike triangles, were not rigid structures it was accepted that the same conditions are unlikely to apply.

The pupils clearly enjoyed this lesson and in the subsequent lesson were able to identify pairs of unconnected congruent triangles, usually quoting the correct conditions. When pupils were asked to produce written proofs for problems involving establishment of the congruence of connected pairs of triangles, only a small minority could do so with minimal teacher intervention. A few made very little progress unaided. However although there was much room for improvement in the written proofs, further practice at this stage would be unlikely to effect this. Pupils were not yet used to the formal language required, and the subject matter is not highly motivating. While there is some value in introducing the conditions for congruent triangles and demonstrating their wider application in simple geometric proofs, this area of mathematics is not the best vehicle for conveying ideas of proof. It does however provide necessary background knowledge for later work.

This discussion, which took about half an hour, can be summarised as follows:–

- Congruent shapes defined as identical and examples drawn on the board.
- Discussion about possible sufficiency of three "matching" sides and/or angles.
- Pupils invited to help – an identical set of three rods given to both pairs of volunteers.
- Demonstrate and explain sufficiency of "three sides" for congruent triangles.
- Repeat with new volunteers to establish sufficiency of SAS.
- Discuss likely sufficiency of "one side and two angles".
- Demonstrate with new volunteers sufficiency with "base" and "base angles" (ASA).
- Discuss and establish sufficiency of "one side and any two angles" (AAS).
- Discuss and reject sufficiency of "an angle and two sides" (ASS!).
- Discuss above ambiguous case with given angle a right angle.
- Establish by discussion sufficiency of "right angle, hypotenuse, side" (RHS).
- Demonstrate and reject the necessary congruency of equiangular triangles.
- Provide written summary.
- (If time) Consider whether "equal sides" necessarily produce congruent quadrilaterals.

Angles in triangles

Most pupils during this phase are familiar with the fact that angles in a triangle sum to 180°. If they are also familiar with other basic angle properties, they may be able to understand a traditional deductive proof about angles in triangles. Either, or both, of the following proofs are appropriate and can be developed with pupils through class discussion, once the initial construction line has been added.

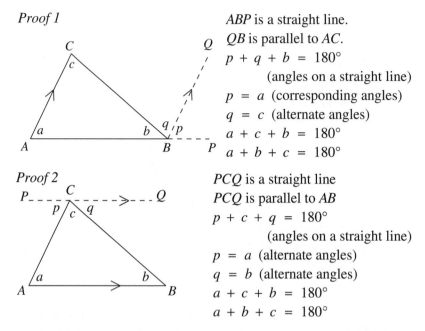

Proof 1

ABP is a straight line.

QB is parallel to *AC*.

$p + q + b = 180°$
(angles on a straight line)

$p = a$ (corresponding angles)

$q = c$ (alternate angles)

$a + c + b = 180°$

$a + b + c = 180°$

Proof 2

PCQ is a straight line

PCQ is parallel to *AB*

$p + c + q = 180°$
(angles on a straight line)

$p = a$ (alternate angles)

$q = b$ (alternate angles)

$a + c + b = 180°$

$a + b + c = 180°$

A third proof, along the same lines as the transformational reasoning approach, has already been described in Chapter 2.

Angles in quadrilaterals and other polygons

A Proof Activity about angles in polygons is described in the next section. However, if time is not available for investigation (followed by an inductive argument based on experimental results then substantiated by a deductive argument) then the deductive argument can be considered as an extension of the above proofs. All quadrilaterals can be perceived as two triangles, leading to an angle sum of $2 \times 180° = 360°$. A class discussion could then proceed along the lines described later.

Pythagoras' theorem

This topic is sometimes introduced to pupils through discovery methods and/or demonstrated by Perigal's dissection, which is illustrated on the pupil worksheet below. The danger of relying only on dissection is well illustrated to pupils by discussion of "A square dissection" described in "Not Proof" at the end of this chapter. The truth of the theorem is usually assumed on the basis of such experimental evidence and pupils are given exercises and problems involving its use. The pupils in the experimental group had been taught in this way two years earlier.

The lesson in which the theorem was to be proved to them began with a class discussion considering the evidence they already had for accepting its truth. This was:–

• *Perigal's dissection*

The diagram, included on the pupil worksheet shown below, served as a reminder of an earlier lesson. Some pupils remembered cutting out and arranging the pieces as shown and feeling that this proved the theorem. On this occasion the fact that this limited the proof to a finite number of cases was mentioned briefly, because there was insufficient time to consider the preferable alternative of the "Square dissection". This is strongly recommended to raise pupil awareness that explanations based only on dissection do not form an acceptable proof.

• *Pythagorean Triples*

Some pupils remembered that triangles with sides 3, 4, and 5 units (and multiples of these) are right-angled and that $3^2 + 4^2 = 5^2$.

• *Measuring*

Some pupils had previously checked that the theorem was true by drawing and measuring right angled triangles. The lesson continued by consideration of the difficulty involved in verifying Pythagoras' theorem for any right-angled triangle by drawing and measuring with reference to a triangle with perpendicular sides of 2.4 cm and 3.5 cm. Calculation, based on the assumption that the theorem is true, gives:–

$$AB^2 = 2.4^2 + 3.5^2 = 18.01$$
$$AB = \sqrt{18.01} = 4.2438.$$

The class seemed to agree that it would be impossible to check this by measuring with a ruler, and that a proof independent of the size of the triangle was needed. The pupil worksheet, though not essential, might be useful at this point in similar discussions.

Proof of Pythagoras' Theorem

The theorem states that:–

the square on the hypotenuse of a right-angled triangle is equal to the sum of the squares on the other two sides.

Not Proof

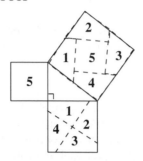

This method is called
Perigal's dissection.

Proof

You will need 8 copies of a right-angled triangle and three squares, one to fit on each side of the triangle.

Use the pieces to make the following diagrams.

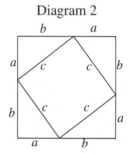

1. Explain carefully how you can be sure that each of this shapes is a square and that they both have exactly the same area.
2. Write down, in terms of a and b, the area of each triangle.
3. Write down, in terms of a, b and c, the total area of each shape.
4. Show that $a^2 + b^2 = c^2$.

   These explanations are independent of the values you chose for a and b and so we can be sure the Pythagoras' Theorem is true for any right-angled triangle.

- *Proof*

   Having summarised the evidence, and appreciated the need for a generalised proof, the pupils were told that they were going to create a proof based on dissection combined with logical reasoning. They were allowed sufficient time to cut out and arrange the pieces as shown in the diagrams. Pupils who might find drawing right-angled shapes difficult could be given squared paper and advised to make the perpendicular sides a whole number of squares.

When the pupils were asked how they knew they had made a square in Diagram 1 the expected response, "Because the sides are equal," was immediately offered, but no-one initially recognised the need to ensure that the shape had four straight sides first. However they accepted this after a class discussion to establish that at each junction the sum of the angles was 180°. It was also readily established through further class discussion that the angles at the vertices were right angles, that the area of the square was $(a + b)^2$ and that this was made up of four triangles (each of area T), a small square (of area a^2) and a medium-sized square (of area b^2). The second diagram was used in a similar way to show that four triangles and large square (of area c^2) could also be fitted together to make a square of area $(a + b)^2$, and that therefore the two squares had equal areas. On this occasion the area of the triangle was designated by T in order that the derivation and use of $T = \frac{1}{2}ab$ should not cloud the main argument.

The pupils were allowed to choose whether to draw Diagrams 1 and 2 or to stick the triangles and squares into their exercise books. Other teachers might prefer to allow pupils to retain the pupil worksheet. Pupils agreed that the shapes were squares because the sides were straight and equal, and because the angles at the vertices were 90°. They were allowed a few minutes to write this in their own words. While they did this the following was written on the board:–

In Diagram 1   Area of square $= (a + b)^2 = a^2 + b^2 + 4T$

In Diagram 2   Area of square $= (a + b)^2 = c^2 + 4T$

So $a^2 + b^2 + 4T = c^2 + 4T$

and $a^2 + b^2 = c^2$

i.e.   Pythagoras' theorem is true for any right-angled triangle

For pupils who are competent in the use of algebra an analysis of Diagram 2, along the following lines, may be appropriate:–

Area of square $= (a + b)^2 = a^2 + 2ab + b^2$

and

Area of square $= c^2 + 4 \times$ area of triangle $= c^2 + 2ab$

Thus $a^2 + 2ab + b^2 = c^2 + 2ab.$

i.e. $a^2 + b^2 = c^2.$

The fact that the above explanation did not depend on the values chosen for a and b, and hence its universal validity, was again emphasised. The difference between this proven dissection and the previous, unproven, Perigal's dissection was also highlighted. Pupils were allowed time to copy the statements on the board into their books, as this was the main part of the proof and it was felt that a copy would be preferable to their own version. Although the complete proof about Diagrams 1 and 2 being squares of equal area had been discussed with pupils, some may only have written a partial proof. This was felt to be sufficient on this occasion because writing a complete proof might hinder rather than enhance their understanding of the proof.

Although the pupils enjoyed the practical aspect of this work and understood the proof, the value of proving something that the pupils have used successfully in the past must be questioned. The difficulty is in deciding whether to defer teaching the use of a theorem or formula until pupils are sufficiently mature to appreciate its proof, to abandon any attempt at proving such mathematical statements, or to attempt a compromise. The preference of the author is for the first option in most instances but this is not always viable as curriculum designers and some other teachers think differently. However, this proof has been used successfully with very able twelve and thirteen year old pupils after they have discovered the relationship described by Pythagoras' theorem, used Perigal's dissection to demonstrate the likely truth of the theorem, and before they have used the theorem.

On another occasion some average thirteen year olds enjoyed making, using squared paper and dimensions 3cm, 4cm, and 5cm (established by measuring), and assembling the two sets of shapes. The class discussion about the completed jigsaw puzzles began by emphasising the fact that it would be about any right-angled triangle, not only the ones they had used. They could forget the measurements of sides (partly because of the use of measuring!) and only needed to remember that one angle was a right-angle. Some pupils could contribute to the class discussion about Diagrams 1 and 2 which was summarised on the board as "These are both squares because the sides are straight and equal, and the corners are right-angles. They are equal in area because the sides are the same length in both," followed by the proof above with T for the area of the original triangle.

Teachers will realise that the above proofs of Pythagoras' theorem are but two of many, some equally suitable for class discussion. A brief search on the Internet revealed twenty-nine different proofs, and references to more. Most of these are based on consideration of equal areas or similar figures. Many of these proofs might be understood by pupils who have been led through one proof of the theorem. Two are include in Chapter 4 where this theorem is revisited with older pupils. A useful homework task for some able younger pupils might be to search the Internet to find and present one proof in their own words. A related homework task, suitable for all pupils, is to ask them to research, either in books or on the Internet, the life of Pythagoras.

Deriving a proof of Pythagoras' theorem is likely to take more than thirty minutes and so the following summary may be helpful:–

- Evaluate evidence to date – Perigal's dissection, Pythagorean triples, Measuring.
- Pupils make pieces for dissection.
- Pupils arrange the pieces as in Diagrams 1 and 2.
- Discuss shape and area of Diagram 1 and then of Diagram 2.
- Compare diagrams to deduce theorem, using algebra if appropriate.
- Pupils complete record of proof in notebooks.
- Emphasise independence of measurements, and hence universality of proof.
- Compare with previous evidence.
- Explain homework task, if required.

Proof Activities

The investigations suggested in this section, although still arising from concrete situations, are more substantial than those in the previous chapter. Lessons and pupil reports based on fourteen activities are described in varying degrees of detail. All are accompanied by pupil worksheets and five also by outline lesson plans. The patterns involved are generally best summarised by algebraic expressions, although use of algebra is not absolutely essential. Pupil worksheets challenge them to find and explain patterns, and then to write a proof to "Convince a penfriend." Many pupils still find writing proofs difficult. It is sensible to accept an informal style of writing, but not to condone lack of precision.

Pupil Challenge

Angles in polygons

A polygon is a plane (two-dimensional) closed shape with straight sides.

1. What is a polygon with a) 3 sides b) 4 sides called?

   a) ....   b) ....

   Name and sketch as many of these as you can.

2. What is a polygon with a) 5 sides; b) 6 sides; c) 8 sides called?

   a) .... b) .... c) ....

3. How many vertices (corners or angles) does a polygon with

   a) 4 sides; b) 7 sides; c) 12 sides have?

   a) .... b) .... c) ....

   What is the relationship between the number of sides and number of angles for any polygon?

   ....

A regular polygon has all its sides the same length and all its angles equal.

What is a regular polygon with 3 sides called?   ....

What is the size of each of its angles?   ....

What is a regular polygon with 4 sides called?   ....

What is the size of each of its angles?   ....

Is there any connection between the sum of all the interior angles of a polygon and the number of sides it has?

Draw regular and irregular 5-sided, 6-sided and 7-sided polygons (six in all) and measure all the interior angles. Calculate the total for each polygon.

Complete the following table.

Number of sides of polygon (n)	Angle sum in degrees
3	
4	
5	
6	
7	

Work in pairs to check, then discuss and write down your answers to the following:–
1. Describe any patterns in this table.
2. Can you predict the angle sum for an 8-sided polygon?
3. Draw a polygon with 8 sides and find the sum of its interior angles.
4. Does it agree with your prediction? Write down a general prediction (conjecture) in terms of n.
5. Check that this agrees with your results for 3, 4, 5, 6, and 7 sided polygons.
6. Write down the angle sum for a polygon with
   a) 12 sides; b) n sides.
7. Does this prove that your conjecture always works?
8. Is it sensible to check for large values of n, e.g.. 50, 100? Give a reason for your answer.
9. Consider how you could justify the above conjecture for a polygon with n sides.

Convince a penfriend.

In this activity finding and explaining the results about angles in polygons is achieved through a blend of teacher exposition to explain the problem, individual pupil activity (possibly a homework assignment) to obtain results, small groups sharing and discussing results, and class discussion to explain the relationships discovered. Finally, pupil reports are also summarised and some quotations included to illustrate the levels of attainment that may be expected at this stage.

The result of the investigation is not obvious and the process of finding it lends itself to a structured approach. The pupil worksheet is designed to revise mathematical vocabulary and to direct the pupils' investigations by structured questions. Spaces are allowed for written responses to questions to encourage active participation of all pupils while the teacher leads a class discussion to introduce the activity. Finally the teacher will explain the problem and ensure that all pupils understand the task of drawing polygons, and that they are then to measure and sum angles. The worksheet is not essential at this stage but pupils will find the structured questions and partially completed tables helpful later.

Lesson Outlines
Angles in polygons

Lesson 1 – Introduction (20 or 60 minutes)

1. (If desired) Class discussion of revision material in pupil worksheet.
2. Pupils draw and measure angles in polygons independently (possibly for homework).
3. Pupils work in pairs or small groups to check results and share ideas.

   (This may take place at the beginning of Lesson 2.)

Lesson 2 – Analysis of results and proof (about 40 minutes)

1. Class discussion to establish/prove angle sum for triangle.
2. Record in table, discussing as appropriate, angle sums for 4, 5, 6, and 7 sided polygons.
3. Raise possibility of alternative unit for angle sums.
4. Pupils work in pairs or small groups to discuss this and structured questions on worksheet.
5. Visit groups.
6. Class discussion to share ideas and consider universal validity of any conjecture in order to establish the need for proof.
7. Why are successive differences 180°?
8. Suggest using triangles.
9. Ask pupils to sketch ideas on board. (At least two methods.)
10. Discuss both methods.
11. Ask pupils to write reports.

Lesson 3 – Extensions

1. Return pupil scripts.
2. Summarise responses and resolve any difficulties.
3. Define exterior angles and discuss sum.
4. Consider sum of interior and exterior angles.
5. Deduce formula/method for finding interior angles of regular polygons.
6. Practice exercises.

Lesson 1 – Introduction

If the introductory revision questions are discussed in detail and pupils allowed to draw polygons and measure angles in class the lesson may take up to about one hour. However if the introduction is curtailed or omitted, and the drawing and measuring set as a homework assignment, then only about twenty minutes are required. In this way both Lessons 1 and 2 could be completed in about one hour.

Teachers should check that their pupils can measure obtuse angles. Pupils should be aware that their measurements of angles are only approximate. All pupils should be encouraged to collect results for at least one regular and one irregular polygon with 5, 6, and 7 sides, before they compare results with others. They can then usefully work in pairs, or small groups to check results. They should find average totals, and begin to discuss the structured questions on the pupil worksheet (or board). They may need reminding to keep a written record of their findings for the next lesson.

Lesson 2 – Analysis of results and proof

At the beginning of a discussion with the experimental group, who had worked from the above worksheet, the angle sum for a triangle was considered. Although all pupils knew that this was $180°$, no-one could explain why. The teacher demonstrated the angle sum by rotating a metre rule about each vertex in turn, and noting that it completed a half-turn. Pupils knew that a complete turn was defined to be $360°$ and so the angle sum for a triangle was deduced.

The pupils also knew that the angle sum for a quadrilateral is $360°$. A few pupils also thought that the angles of a pentagon added up to $360°$. However they had confused the interior angles of the pentagon with the angles at the centre of a regular pentagon! They had previously been reminded that they would need to divide the angle at the centre of the circumscribing circle into five equal angles of $72°$ to draw a regular pentagon. However others had totals of around $540°$ and these were recorded on the board. The minority group above readily appreciated the error they had made.

Several pupils suggested that the angle sum for a hexagon was $720°$ indicating that they had met this in earlier work. For a seven-sided figure several values around $900°$ were offered and all recorded. Pupils were then reminded that they would need to calculate average values. They were told to work individually or in pairs to consider an alternative unit for giving the angle totals. They could then review their answers to the structured questions in the light of results on the board.

Many pupils noticed that the difference between successive totals was 180° and had no difficulty in using this to predict an angle sum for an octagon. There were two main methods for checking this prediction. Most drew either a regular or irregular octagon and measured the angles. Two girls claimed to have checked it by means of a sketch. This was valid because they had used the sides and diagonals of the squares in their books as sides of the octagon and were able to explain that each angle comprised a right-angle and 45° making the angles 135° each and therefore the total was eight times this (1080°). One boy said that the total was 1080° because it fitted the pattern but immediately saw the flaw in this statement and agreed the need to check by measuring at this stage. Most pupils were also able to find a formula, $S = (n - 2) \times 180°$, with little or no teacher intervention, and to check that it agreed with measured values.

At the beginning of a class discussion to raise awareness of the need for a proof the pupils were asked whether the formula above would always be true. Opinion was divided. One boy changed his mind twice. His initial reaction was that it might not always be true, but when he saw that others disagreed with this he agreed with them. Then he thought again and said that it might not be true for large n. The possibility of checking this was discussed and one pupil suggested drawing and measuring. When asked whether this would cause any difficulties he said that it would take a long time and probably not be very accurate. Eventually the need for a proof was agreed.

The pupils were asked for an explanation as to why successive differences in the table should be 180.° No-one responded, even though they knew that the shape whose angle sum was 180° was a triangle. The possibility of dividing other polygons into triangles was suggested. They should not be overlapping as this had caused some difficulties on a previous occasion. One boy said that each vertex could be joined to a point inside the shape and this was sketched on the board. When they were asked whether there was another method a girl volunteered to draw her idea. She joined two vertices and then joined a third to a point near the middle of this line before realising that it was essentially the same method. Another pupil was able to suggest joining one vertex to all the other vertices and this was also drawn on the board.

The two methods were compared. In the first it was agreed that the number of triangles was the same as the number of sides but that other angles had been introduced. The pupils readily recognised that these were the angles at the centre, that their sum was 360°, and that this was twice 180°. The second method had the advantage that no extra angles were introduced but the number of triangles was not the same as the number of sides. However there were no problems for the pupils in seeing that the number of triangles was two less than the number of sides.

No formal proof was written on the board but the pupils were reminded that their written reports should include a proof based on one of the above arguments. They were given the following worksheet to help them.

Angles in polygons – Proof

Proof of conjecture

Consider how any polygon can be divided into non-overlapping triangles.

Draw a diagram to show your method.

Copy and complete the following table:–

Number of sides	Number of triangles
3	
4	
etc	

Compare this with your table of angle sums.

Explain the connection with your conjecture for the angle sum for an n-sided polygon.

Extensions

1.   Consider the size of each angle in a regular polygon.

2.   Investigate exterior angle sums.

Conclusions/Formulae

For any polygon with n sides:–

Sum of interior angles = ...

Sum of exterior angles = ...

For a regular polygon with n sides:–

Each interior angle = ...

Each exterior angle = ...

Report

Write a full report on your investigation (with extensions if possible) to include:

an initial question;

diagrams indicating angles measured;

summary of results (in a table)

analysis and discussion of results leading to a conjecture (see above for guidance);

proof that your conjecture is always true (see above for guidance);

Remember – This explanation should **"convince a penfriend"**.

Some of them would also be expected to include consideration of the extensions suggested in the worksheet: namely the size of an interior angle of a regular polygon, or the exterior angles of polygons.

Pupil reports

In nearly half of the reports, pupils described the expected pattern, made and tested a conjecture, acknowledged the need for proof and made some attempt to provide a proof. About one half of these reports were exemplary and included well-expressed proofs. The remainder showed awareness of the need for proof but pupils were unable to construct one completely in general terms. However they were moving towards the use of proof by providing a detailed explanation of why the formula they quoted worked for a particular case, or explaining part of their formula in general terms.

The following three pupil comments illustrate this transition state towards fully understanding, and using confidently, the notion of proof:–

KB: "I don't think the previous examples are really enough to prove that it will always work because I haven't taken large   numbers into account;" [followed by an incorrect general explanation based on use of triangles, and then], "From all the previous information I cannot be sure but I am fairly confident that for a polygon with n sides the angle sum is $(n - 2) \times 180°$."

This pupil was clearly aware of the need for proof but not quite capable on this occasion of producing a correct proof.

LB: "I'm still not convinced it is correct as it has only been tested on small numbers. It would need to be tested on large numbers but this would take too long."

There was no mention of proof but this pupil is aware that testing a few values is not a proof.

TS: "This formula has not been fully proved;" [followed by analysis of the interior and exterior angles of a pentagon and a conclusion that], "This proves the formulae are true."

It is possible that this pupil confused a pentagon with a polygon but equally likely that there is still slight confusion between proof and demonstration.

Three pupils, who were confident in both appreciation and use of proof wrote:–

KW: "Showing that the conjecture works for 3, 4, 5, 6, and 7 does not prove it always works, but I believe it probably would;" [followed by a satisfactory explanation of how the formula related to dividing a polygon radially into triangles].

CJ: "It is sensible to check for large n because there might be a point where the formula ceases to be correct;" [followed by a well explained proof based on dividing a polygon into triangles by diagonals from one vertex].

CS: "We do not yet have enough information that my formula works. If I need to be sure I need to look at why it works – therefore proving when it will and won't work;" [followed by good explanations and diagrams relating to a hexagon, as a "thought experiment" (Balacheff, 1988), and a generalisation of the results including] "The triangles will have '180°' worth of angles in them and there are two less triangles than there are sides."

The style of correct explanations ranged from that of a boy who wrote the whole report in formal mathematical language to the informal style used by a boy who wrote:–

DK: "We subtract two because the two lines being subtracted wouldn't have any value as they couldn't form a polygon whereas three and above can. Every 180° in a polygon is equivalent to a triangle. The number of triangles agrees with the column ' ÷ 180 '."

In contrast, there were six pupils who made no reference to proof and four who confused demonstration and proof. The group of six included one boy who noted that there were $n - 2$ triangles in a polygon and the angle sum was $(n - 2)\,180°$ but did not state or imply the connection between the statements. Examples of those confusing proof and demonstration are the girl and boy who, having checked that the formula worked for particular values wrote, "This proves my conjecture" and "It seems that my conjecture always works."

Lesson 3 – Extensions

On this occasion sufficient time had been spent on the sum of interior angles of polygons, as all pupils had identified a correct relationship and most had made some attempt to justify it. So the following lesson began with the return of pupil reports with general comments. It continued by considering the exterior angles of polygons, and then regular polygons, as few pupils had included these in their reports. The fact that exterior angles sum to 360° was established using transformational reasoning based on "mentally walking round" a polygon, and noting that the turning involved at the vertices was equivalent to a complete turn. Consideration of the sum of all exterior and interior angles, using previously proven results, provided a more formal deductive proof. The formula (or method) for finding angles in regular polygons was also deduced through class discussion. Pupils were then provided with exercises to practise using these results.

Pupil Challenge

Staircase numbers

A staircase number is formed by
adding consecutive integers.

Examples:–

12 because $3 + 4 + 5 = 12$ (3-step)

53 because $26 + 27 = 53$ (2-step)

80 because $14 + 15 + 16 + 17$
$= 80$ (4-step)

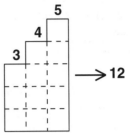

Investigate staircase numbers and try to answer the following
questions.

1. What do you notice about
   (i) 3-step numbers, (ii) 5-step, (iii) 7-step numbers?
2. What about any "odd-step" staircase number?
3. Can you explain this result?
4. Do "even-step" staircase numbers behave in the same way?
5. Explain.
6. Describe how to find a staircase for a number.
7. Is it possible to find more than one staircase?
8. Are there any numbers which are not staircase numbers?
   If so, which?

Write a report about your investigation to
convince a penfriend.

This is a straightforward investigation into the factors of numbers
formed by adding sets of consecutive integers, which all pupils
expected to start confidently. Porteous (1986) used an explanation of
the fact that the sum of three such integers is divisible by three in a
questionnaire given to pupils aged eleven to sixteen. She found that
nearly one quarter could understand the proof and/or create a proof.
So this was an appropriate proof activity for pupils in the
experimental group, with whom an algebraic proof could be
discussed alongside diagrammatic or other proofs.

Although the pupil worksheet includes structured questions the
pupils were told that the questions were to guide their investigation

but need not be answered in strict order. They were intended to highlight the existence of patterns and encourage pupils to analyse why they occur. It was expected that pupils would recognise odd multiples from "odd-step" numbers and possibly appreciate why they occurred.

Lesson Outlines

Staircase numbers

Lesson 1 – Introduction (1 hour)

1. Short introductory discussion to explain task.
2. Pupils begin investigating "odd-step" numbers alone or in pairs for about ten minutes.
3. Class discussion about "three-step" numbers
4. Draw a staircase (4 + 5 + 6 = 15) on the board and ask pupils to explain.
5. Consider another method of describing numbers in general – Algebra.
6. Pupils then continue their investigations for about half an hour.
7. Class discussion:–

   (i) listing examples of four-step numbers

   (ii) describing patterns – twice the sum of the middle two terms and four times the number halfway between the middle two terms.
8. Algebraic argument to established the equivalence of these two descriptions and the generalisation to a formula.
9. Find a staircase for a given number, say 35.
10. Written (interim) report (if appropriate).

Lesson 2 – Follow-up discussion (30 minutes)

1. Reminder about how staircase numbers are found.
2. Find a staircase using factors.
3. Ask for pairs of numbers that multiply to give 24:– 2 × 12 not possible, 3 × 8 gives "three-step" staircase, 6 × 4 not possible.
4. Conclusion: – the number in question must have at least one odd factor.
5. Can 24 be an eight-step number?
6. Further discussion to establish need for odd factors for more that one staircase.

7. Non-staircase numbers (1, 2, 4, 8, ...) listed on the board.
8. Pattern discussed – repeated doubling, powers of two.
9. Conclusion:– they have no odd factors.
10. Possible extensions –
    Could zero be a step? What about negative numbers?
11. Written report (if appropriate).

Lesson 1 – Introduction

The pupils were given the worksheet. The lesson began with a short introductory discussion to ensure that all understood the definition and could begin investigating "odd-step" numbers. Some worked alone and some in pairs, for about ten minutes, calculating results and looking for patterns.

Class discussion on three-step numbers produced three suggestions:– three times the middle step; the first step times three add three; and three times last step take away three. A staircase showing $4 + 5 + 6 = 15$ was drawn on the board and the pupils asked to explain the first suggestion. One pupil's explanation was to take one from the six column over to the four column to leave three columns of five, which was understood by the rest of the class. The class agreed this would be true for any three-step number. In order to explain the other suggestions another method of describing numbers in general had to be used and pupils suggested Algebra, Formulae, and Letters. The discussion began with pupil suggestions that the numbers could be represented by n, $n + 1$, and $n + 2$. and established that all three-step numbers could be written as $3(n + 1)$ which agreed with the second suggestion above; and went further to show that this was the same as $3(n + 2) - 3$ to explain the last suggestion above.

Pupils then continued their investigations for about half an hour, after which a class discussion began by listing some examples of four-step numbers on the board and asking pupils to describe any patterns they had found. One pupil suggested they were twice the sum of the middle two terms and another they they were four times the number halfway between the middle two terms. The pupils were able to follow and contribute to the algebraic argument that established the equivalence of these two descriptions and the generalisation to a formula that applied to all "even-step" numbers.

The discussion concluded by consideration of how to find a staircase for a given number, say 35. There was no response for a while and then an audible whisper from one of the weaker pupils (Claire) asserted, "This is hard." In response to the question, "Is it a three-step staircase?" many of the pupils' reactions clearly demonstrated that they had understood the implication of the question and had no difficulty in giving a correct answer. It was also clear a few seconds later that Claire realised the connection between factors and staircase numbers and was able to explain that 35 was not a three-step number because three did not divide into it. It was then easily established that 35 was a five-step number with a middle step of seven and also a seven step number with a middle step of five.

At the end of the lesson the pupils were reminded that they had to write a report of their investigations for homework. This activity, with class discussion of five and seven-step numbers as well as three-step ones, and briefer consideration of "even-step" numbers, has since been successfully used with twelve and thirteen year old pupils of average ability, as a link between lessons on Number topics and lessons on algebra. They were able to contribute to discussions about the diagrammatic and algebraic arguments but they were not asked to write a report about these.

Pupil reports

Most reports from the pupils in the experimental group included a satisfactory explanation of the structure of "odd-step" numbers – some used algebra, some diagrams and some both. About half also explained "even-step" numbers, and compared them with "odd-step" numbers. One pupil devised her own explanation with a diagram showing an even-step staircase divided in half vertically to show that it was the product of half the number of steps and the sum of the middle two numbers. About one third described the rôle of factors, how to construct a staircase and when more than one was possible. Few made significant progress in identifying non-staircase numbers (those with only even factors) and none could explain satisfactorily the pattern of the ones they found.

The following is an extract from a report written by a very able twelve year old girl in the class with whom the activity was first trialled.

Gilly's explanation

'Odd-step numbers are all multiples of the number of steps in the staircase. Also if you multiply the middle number by the number of steps you will get the result. The numbers on the left of the middle number are the same amount less than the middle number as the ones on the right are more. This means you have however many steps multiplied by the middle number as the sides balance each other out.

Even-step numbers do not behave in exactly the same way as they are dealing with halves. If you take the middle of the two numbers and multiply this by the number of steps you get the answer $(1 + 2 = 3 = 1\frac{1}{2} \times 2)$ This is not automatically recognised as the two times table because it is a half. But because it is an even number there is not one middle number but two."

This is not a mathematically rigorous proof but it does demonstrate an appreciation of the notion of proof and an understanding of the essence of the problem.

Lesson 2 – Follow-up discussion

This began with the reminder that staircase numbers were the product of the number of steps and the middle number, as the written reports had demonstrated that all pupils appreciated this fact. When asked what they should do first when finding a staircase some pupils suggested finding a factor of the number although they had various ways of expressing this. It was clear from the reactions of others that they understood the idea but had been unable to put it into words. All appreciated that the factor chosen would be the number of steps of the staircase.

The class was then asked for pairs of numbers that multiplied to give 24, with the intention of finding its staircase. The first suggestion was 2×12. When asked to find a staircase based on this product they tried to produce one but could not. No pupil was confident enough to say there wasn't one or to explain why it might be impossible to find one. However they clearly understood, when it was suggested to them, that the lack of a middle integer caused the problem. Given more time a pupil might have discovered this without prompting. Consideration of 24 as 3×8 immediately led to the recognition that it was a "three-step staircase" number, and then as 4×6 to the realisation that this did not produce a possible staircase.

When asked what conclusion they could draw from this a few were able to explain that the number in question must have at least one odd factor.

The class was then reminded of the earlier discussion which had established 35 as either a five- or seven-step number and asked whether 24 could be an eight-step as well as a three-step number. Some were able to explain that this was impossible because an eight-step number did not have a middle integer. Further discussion established that only numbers which could be written as a product with odd factors had more that one staircase.

The pupils were then asked for any non-staircase numbers they had found and these (1, 2, 4, 8, ...) were listed on the board. The pattern was immediately recognised as repeated doubling, and eventually as powers of two. When asked why these should be non-staircase numbers a few pupils were able to see that they had no odd factors.

Near the end of the lesson pupils were invited to ask any questions that might extend the investigation. One boy asked whether zero could be a step and agreed that it could be useful if one wanted to include one as a staircase number. Another boy, possibly provoked by the previous question and answer, wondered whether negative numbers could be included. He was asked to consider 22 as a staircase number and appreciated that it could not be a two-step number with eleven in the middle, nor an eleven-step number with two in the middle if only positive numbers were allowed. He was keen to express his understanding of this and explained that if two were the middle number out of eleven the staircase would have to start with a negative number.

Although some of the questions in the above discussion were only answerable by a few pupils most of the class seemed to understand the answers and appreciate the general argument, and many made a valid contribution. Their responses indicate that pupils of this age and ability do not naturally analyse mathematical patterns but are capable of being led through such analysis and enjoy a sense of achievement when they understand it.

Pupil Challenge

Triangle numbers

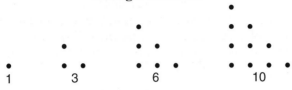

1   3   6   10

The first four triangle numbers are shown above.

Use the following questions to guide your investigation and write a report.

1. By drawing similar diagrams find the next three triangle numbers and continue this table.

Position	Triangle number
(*n*)	(*T*)
1	1
2	3
3	...
4	...
...	...

2. Write down the next three triangle numbers after the last one you have drawn.

3. Explain how you could obtain the 20th triangle number.

4. Find the most efficient way of doing this.

5. Test it on some triangle numbers you have found.

6. Try to write your method as a formula for finding the *n*th triangle number *T*.

7. Test your formula for *n* = 2, 3, and 4.

8. Explain how and why your formula works for the fifth triangle number.

9. Will it always work? How can you be sure.

Convince a penfriend.

This is a good example of a non-linear, but easily obtainable, number pattern which can be proved in a spatial context. The pupil worksheet begins by advising that the questions should only be used to guide their investigation and report because, although some pupils need such a framework, the thinking of others might be inhibited by its imposition. A partially completed table of results is included to encourage the pupils to tabulate their results in the hope of increasing the likelihood of them spotting any patterns. The variables n and T are introduced to avoid possible confusion in class discussion.

Lesson Outlines

Triangle numbers

Lesson 1 – Introduction (30 – 40 minutes)

1. Explain the task.
2. Pupils investigate the problem independently for about ten to fifteen minutes.
3. Class discussion to share ideas.
4. Pupils continue and write reports for homework.
   (30 – 40 minutes)

Lesson 2 – Follow-up discussion (20 – 30 minutes)

1. Triangle numbers (T) tabulated against their corresponding integers (n).
2. Ask for a method for finding triangle numbers.
3. Improve on the method.
4. Examine differences between consecutive triangle numbers.
5. Discuss relationships between T and n, e.g. $T - n$; T / n.
6. If necessary, ask direct questions, e.g. How many halves?
7. Discuss a particular example, e.g. $T_4 / 4 = (4 + 1) \times \frac{1}{2}$, and progress to a generalisation.
8. Highlight the difference between testing a formula, and proving it.
9. Explain why the formulae always work – using explanations, with diagrams, quoted from the pupil reports.

Lesson 1 – Introduction

The pupils in the experimental group were each given a worksheet and told to explore the problem independently. For about ten minutes they were almost completely silent. Then one girl said, with obvious pleasure, that she had found a formula. Inspection of her work revealed that she had written $n(n + 1)$ but she had some difficulty in explaining exactly what she meant. Another girl nearby, who had overheard this conversation, said that she too had a similar idea and was able to explain her thinking slightly more clearly than the first girl as she had a table of results with some arrows to illustrate her thoughts. The class then continued their investigations, but now discussing their ideas with each other. After a few more minutes ideas were shared in a class discussion.

At the beginning of the class discussion the pupils were able to provide the first ten triangle numbers (T) which were tabulated against their corresponding integers (n). When they were asked for a method of obtaining triangle numbers the second girl described above volunteered to come to the board and explain her method to the class. She added arrows across the table on the board to show that $1 + 2 = 3$, $3 + 3 = 6$, $6 + 4 = 10$, ... and explained that each of the triangle numbers was formed by "adding the next integer to the last triangle number." The first girl described above claimed that this was the same as her method and there was almost an argument as to who thought of it first. (It is good to see emotions aroused in a mathematics classroom – provided they can be controlled!) Later inspection of her work revealed that she had considered differences between successive triangle numbers and that her initial attempt at a formula should have read nth number $+ (n - 1)$th triangle number. She had formed a clear understanding of this result by the time of the second discussion of her work.

When the class was asked if they could improve on the method above the only responses at first were reiterations of the first method. A girl explained that the fourth triangle number could be made by adding a row of four dots to the array for the third number and this idea was readily extended to establish that triangle numbers were formed by adding consecutive integers. This reference to the diagrams was a tailor-made opportunity to highlight their value in trying to explain any formulae they were able to find. As the lesson ended at this point they were told to continue these investigation and write a report for homework.

Pupil reports

Not surprisingly all reports established that triangle numbers were made by adding consecutive integers and calculated the twentieth number in this way. One boy even appeared to have found the hundredth by addition. Two pupils quoted a "formula" for adding consecutive integers. One used $T = n + t$ but did not define t

although it was clear from the report, which referred to the rows of dots, that it represented "the previous triangle number." The other pupil explained that they were formed by adding the next integer to the total so far and quoted this as $t = n + < n$. Although it is gratifying to see pupils confident enough to attempt the use of algebra they clearly need to be reminded of the importance of defining any terms they use.

Only the above three reports relied entirely on repeated addition. Another boy suggested that an improvement to this method for finding the twentieth triangle number was to start from the tenth and then add the "remaining integers." His report continued by considering odd and even integers separately and established that the twentieth triangle number could be calculated as 20×10.5. He was able to generalise this result and explained that "the multiplier is ½ the number + ½" giving the expression for finding the nth triangle number (T_n) as $n \times (\tfrac{1}{2}n + \tfrac{1}{2})$.

Another pupil began very promisingly by explaining that when n was odd it was a factor of T and when n was even $n + 1$ was a factor of T. However, having quoted an example of each, he continued, "…. but first I need a formula to explain this," and produced $T = \tfrac{1}{2}n \times (n + 1)$. He concluded by explaining that the product $n(n + 1)$ is halved because a triangle is half a square but he is clearly confusing derivation and explanation of a formula. Two other reports included good descriptions of finding T_n as $\tfrac{1}{2}n(n + 1)$ by reference to the table of results.

In all other reports the formula $T = \tfrac{1}{2}n(n + 1)$, or an equivalent statement, appeared without previous explanation but was used correctly to test values already obtained and to find T_{100}. However about one third of these included an attempt at a justification of the formula later. Of these two pupils related triangle numbers to half a square (n^2) but were confused about the rôle of +1. Another, attempting to justify $T = \tfrac{1}{2}n^2 + \tfrac{1}{2}n$, described T_{12} as two square arrays of 6 by 6 because 6 was half of 12 but she forgot to include $+\tfrac{1}{2} \times 12$. A third pupil described T_{12} as "the larger half of a 12 by 12 square and the other half is the eleventh triangle number." He continued by considering the product $\tfrac{1}{2}(12 \times 13)$ but was confused as to whether this represented the twelfth or thirteenth triangle number.

Four pupils produced valid proofs of the formula they quoted. Two pupils used a diagram showing two triangular arrays for T_4

arranged to form a rectangular array 4 by 5 and explained in general terms that this demonstrated that T_n was half of a similar array n by $(n + 1)$ and thus proved that $T_n = \frac{1}{2}n(n + 1)$. One girl, in justifying the result $T = \frac{1}{2}n^2 + \frac{1}{2}n$ for T_{12}, drew a 12 by 12 square array and explained that half of this would only include half the dots on the diagonal and that therefore it was necessary to add half of twelve to the result. The fourth proof did not refer to a diagram but explained that the integers in each sum could be paired from each end of the sum giving $n / 2$ pairs each with a total of $n + 1$ and thus an overall total of $\frac{n}{2} \times (n + 1)$. (He failed to realise that n might be odd.)

Most pupils did not attempt to prove a formula although a few thought that demonstrating validity for particular examples was sufficient proof. One boy stated: "The formula always works because it works for the numbers tested so far." It was therefore necessary to emphasise the distinction between proof and demonstration in the next lesson as well as to provide a strategy for deriving a formula.

Lesson 2 – Follow-up discussion

At the beginning of the lesson the pupils were congratulated on the fact that they had all completed the first part of the investigation successfully and clearly appreciated the value of a formula for finding large triangle numbers. When it was suggested that they could have copied the formula they had quoted there was embarrassed agreement. The aim of the first part of the lesson was to demonstrate a systematic approach to looking for patterns in order to derive a formula.

The analysis of the number pattern began by examining successive differences between the triangle numbers to establish that each was the sum of all preceding integers, and confirming this by calculating values of $T - n$. Although it could be argued that it was unnecessary to consider this latter it was included as a straightforward example of a comparison of T with n before the more difficult concept of the ratio T / n was introduced.

As the pupils calculated the ratio for themselves they were quick to perceive that it increased in halves but slow to relate it back to the values of n. (This is a good example of pupils being much better at spotting patterns down the columns of a table than across its rows.) When asked directly how many halves there were it was the third pupil who gave a full correct response that the required number was the next integer. Once it was drawn to their attention the rest of the pupils   readily   understood   a   particular   example   e.g. $T_4/4 = (4 + 1) \times \frac{1}{2}$, and progressed easily to a generalisation and rearrangement of this result to give the formula that most of them had quoted. During this discussion some pupils had been obviously interested and others, though appearing not to be involved at times, made valuable contributions to the discussion.

The lesson continued by highlighting the difference between testing a formula, and proving it. The pupils were asked to consider the tediousness of testing whether or not their value of T_{100} obtained using a formula was correct. This seemed to persuade them of the value of an argument independent of a particular triangle number. The remainder of the class discussion focussed on explaining why the formulae always worked. This was achieved by using the explanations quoted above from the pupil reports, with their authors' involvement if they were willing, and able to explain their thinking clearly to the class; and diagrams as shown below, on the board:–

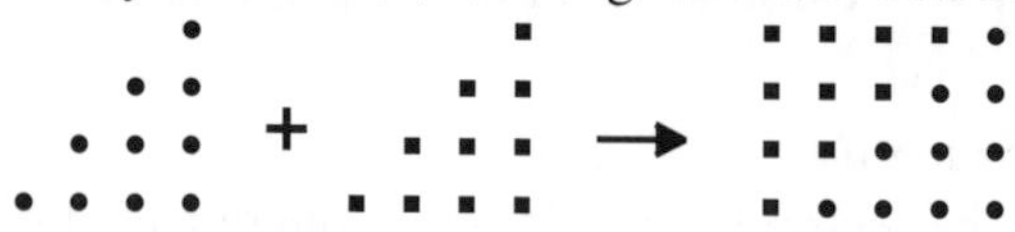

$$2T_4 = 4 \times 5$$
$$T_4 = \tfrac{1}{2}(4 \times 5)$$
$$T_n = \tfrac{1}{2}n(n + 1)$$

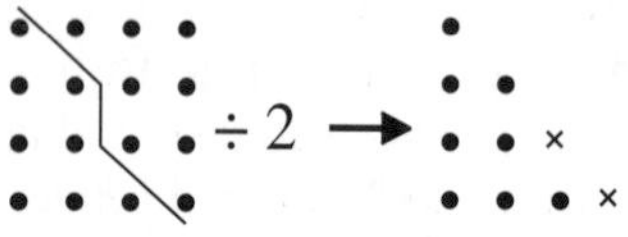

$$4^2 \div 2 = T_4 - \tfrac{4}{2}$$
$$T_4 = 4^2 + \tfrac{4}{2}$$
$$T_n = \tfrac{n^2}{2} + \tfrac{n}{2}$$

For the method of adding consecutive integers by pairing from each end the diagram in Chapter 2 was also drawn, as these pupils had not seen it previously.

Pupil Challenge

Crossing lines

Two non-parallel straight lines intersect once.

2 lines
1 point of intersection

Three non-parallel straight lines have a maximum of three intersections

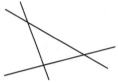

3 lines
1 point of
intersection

Investigate the maximum number of intersections (I) for any number (n) of lines.

Try to find a connection between the number of lines and the number of intersections.

Can you find a formula?

Explain why your connection/formula always works.

Convince a penfriend.

This investigation involves finding the maximum number of intersections formed by an increasing number of straight lines and was suggested by Brown (1995) as practice in producing convincing arguments. The pattern involved is the set of triangle numbers so this challenge should come after the previous activity. Although a pupil worksheet is included experience suggests that this investigation is best introduced to pupils with diagrams on the board. In that way the need to draw non-parallel lines, and to extend all lines to intersect others can both be emphasised.

Because of the similarity of these discussions to the previous discussions about "Handshakes" and "Triangle Numbers" separate Lesson Outlines are not included here, but the responses of the pupils in the experimental group are summarised.

Lesson 1 – Introduction

At the beginning of this lesson the pupils in the experimental group were reminded that they would be expected to write a report using headings written on the board:– Problem, Plan, Results, Patterns leading to Formulae, and Proof. The brief instructions here, as opposed to lists of questions in previous investigations in this phase, may not be sufficient for all pupils. For some pupils, however, concise instructions may make the task seem more accessible. They also provide variety of approach, and may encourage some degree of independence in problem solving. This lesson took place with the experimental group several weeks after the work on triangle numbers.

After an explanation of this task the pupils had no difficulty in obtaining correct results for four lines. However on other occasions some pupils have drawn parallel lines, and others have failed to produce lines to create the maximum number of intersections for four lines. During the rest of the lesson pupils added more lines and considered the results without further teacher intervention. After a few minutes at least one girl had already obtained a correct formula. Finding a formula is perceived by many pupils to be the principal aim of such activities. The pupils were reminded that they should try to explain any formulae they use/find and to include this in their reports, which were to be written for homework.

Pupil reports

Although most pupils had some correct results nearly half also included some errors, mainly as a result of not producing non-parallel lines until they intersected, but they were still able to find patterns and make some valid deductions.

Ten pupils investigated successive differences in the number of intersections and noticed that these were consecutive integers but only three of these extended this idea to establish that the number of intersections for n lines is the sum of integers to $n - 1$. One pupil correctly indicated on his table of results that, for instance $n_1 + n_2 = I_3$ but in writing down the results used I without a suffix to represent all values of I and so was unable to establish the result above.

Five pupils quoted the formula $I = \frac{1}{2}n(n - 1)$ but only two explained its derivation from number patterns in the results. One of these and another pupil were able to explain the connection with the diagrams: "Each line crosses every other line ..... $n(n - 1)$ .... and we divide by two because we have counted each intersection twice;" and, "The number of intersections per line is $n - 1$ and so we multiply by n and we divide by two because the lines share intersections." One pupil who quoted a correct formula, but who did not explain its derivation, explained the presence of $n - 1$ by saying, "The number of intersections rises by the previous number of lines." He failed to appreciate that this was an explanation of adding $n - 1$ and not multiplying by it.

The reports show that most pupils are attempting to describe patterns and relate them to formulae, and/or explain how their formulae relate to the original problem. Only one pupil confused demonstration by substitution with proof.

Lesson 2 – Follow-up discussion

The class discussion began with a table of results of n and I and an invitation to describe any patterns in the values for I. One girl, whose original results had been incorrect, became very excited and was keen to explain that the differences increased by one each time. When asked if this idea could be used to find a relationship between n and I one boy explained that $n - 1$, $n - 2$ down to 1 had to be added, (He had written this in his report.) and was happy for this to be written on the board as $1 + 2 + 3 + ... + (n - 1)$. As on a previous occasion, when finding a formula for triangle numbers, the pupils agreed that a better method may be available but no-one appeared to recognise the presence of triangle numbers. (They were not mentioned at this juncture to prevent unnecessary confusion.) It was suggested that they found I/n and they readily identified this as $n - 1$ halves and thus a formula was obtained.

In order to relate this to the diagrams they were asked how many lines the third line and fourth line crossed. Several could then explain that the nth line would cross $n - 1$" others leading to $n(n - 1)$ and some were able to explain the reason for dividing by two and this seemed to be understood by the rest.

At this point they were asked if they recognised the numbers in the results for the number of intersections and a few realised they were triangle numbers and the rest of the class then clearly remembered them. It was established that the $(n - 1)$th triangle number was the number of intersections for n lines and this was found using the formula previously found for the nth triangle number and compared with the formula for I. This point was not laboured as the pupils had reached "saturation point". In some classes it may be appropriate to re-establish the link with the sum of consecutive integers.

The *DIME Pre-algebra Project booklets* (Giles, 1984) provide a useful source of patterns with a visual structure which pupils can reasonably be expected to analyse independently for homework. Each pattern is accompanied by a set of numerical mappings for pupils to complete and from which they are expected to deduce a formula. Although intended for younger pupils, the requests to explain the relationships between the structure and formula for the mappings provided work of a suitable standard for the pupils in the experimental group. These able fourteen and fifteen year old pupils had only recently been introduced to the notion of proof and some were still finding the writing of explanations difficult. The inclusion of the partially completed tables on the pupil worksheets was to allow all pupils to achieve at least a record of results. It was also expected that most would be able to derive at least one formula. Again, however, the use of algebra is not essential for describing the patterns.

Pupil Challenge

Hydrocarbons

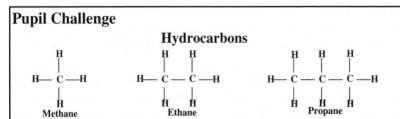

Methane   Ethane   Propane

Atoms of carbon combine with atoms of hydrogen to form various hydrocarbon molecules. These diagrams show the structures of some "straight-chain" hydrocarbons. You may recognise some of their names. If you know the chemical formulae write them in the last column of the table below.

Name	Number of carbon atoms (C)	Number of hydrogen atoms (H)	Number of bonds (B) (lines)	Chemical formula (optional)
Methane	1	4	4	CH_4
Ethane	2	6	7	
Propane	3			
Butane	4			
Pentane	5			
Decane	10			
Hectane	100			

1. Copy and complete the table.
2. Describe the connection relating H and C, and the connection relating B and C, in words.
3. Explain how you found each pattern.
4. Write each pattern as an algebraic formula.
5. Explain why each of your formulae works for any number of carbon atoms.

Convince a penfriend.

This activity was selected partly because of its cross-curricular nature. An ideal is to introduce it soon after pupils have met the same topic in Chemistry. The patterns involved are linear and provide practice at a suitable level in pattern spotting. An important property of the relationships between the variables is that the formulae can be explained by relating them to the diagrams in several different ways which Brown (1995) considers to be an "attractive feature" of some patterns. Additionally the patterns are not too complex to describe in words, although many pupils may find this difficult without help.

The assignment was set as homework for the experimental group in the first instance. The worksheet for the homework assignment was given out near the end of a lesson allowing time for verbal instructions and any additional clarifications that the pupils needed as they read through the instructions. This has since been used as a class activity for very able thirteen and fourteen year old pupils and also slightly less able fourteen year old pupils. The following outline summarises these lessons.

Lesson Outline (30 – 40 minutes)
Hydrocarbons
1. Explain the task.
2. Pupils work individually, or in pairs, to collect and tabulate results.
3. Using table on board, discuss number patterns for H.
4. Summarise connections on board.
5. Derive formula(e), and discuss equivalence, if appropriate.
6. Repeat 3 to 5 for B.
7. Discuss relationship between verbal statement of connection, or formula, for H and diagram.
8. Repeat 7 for B – a longer discussion.
9. Consider alternative formulae – explain and discuss equivalence.
10. Written reports.

    (2 and 10 could be set for homework as preparation for class discussion, 3 to 9.)

Pupil reports

Although most pupils in the experimental group obtained a correct algebraic formula some had difficulty in explaining satisfactorily how they arrived at it. They used phrases like, "Careful observation," and "Looking at the numbers, I noticed that ... ." Many noticed patterns down the columns such as that the successive differences between the number of carbon atoms (C) and numbers of hydrogen atoms (H) increased by one, and successive differences between values of H increased by two. One boy divided C by H and noticed that the results for C = 3, 4, and 5, namely "two remainder two", also applied to C=1 and C=2. He approached the number of bonds in the same way and succeeded in obtaining both formulae. Only four pupils did not obtain correct formulae, e.g.. H=2C+2, B= 3C+1, and of these two noticed that "B=H+C−1", but were unable to proceed further.

Nearly one third of the pupils recognised and explained the relationship between both formulae and the structure of the hydrocarbon molecules by reference to the diagrams. Another third explained one formula or part of both, such as the pupil who explained why C was multiplied by two (for H) and three (for B) but not why two and one were added. A few pupils obtained the formula B=8+2(C−2). They had noticed that the carbon atoms on the ends had four bonds each and the ones in the middle were attached to two hydrogen molecules but failed to notice the bonds between carbon atoms. One pupil adopted this approach correctly and obtained B=8+ 2(C−2)+C−1−2, and was also able to explain the formula B=3C+1 which he had obtained from the table. He did not however try to reconcile these two formulae and this served as a useful point of discussion in the next lesson. Some of the remaining pupils justified their formulae by substituting values of C. They are clearly still confusing proof with demonstration.

Lesson – Follow-up discussion

The first part of the next lesson was spent in a class discussion of the derivation and explanation of the various formulae. Pupils agreed that successive values of H (for C=1, 2, 3, 4, and 5) increased by two and that this suggested finding 2C. Examination of the values of 2C showed them to be two less than H each time, which indicated that + 2 should be included in the formula. Two sentences to this effect were written on the board to provide an appropriate form of words for those pupils who had found this difficult. The equivalence of H= 2C+2 and H=2(C+1) was raised and discussed. The formula for the number of bonds was established and described in a similar way.

The relationship between the formula H = 2C + 2 and the diagrams was explained by several pupils along the lines, "Double C because there are hydrogen atoms above and below each carbon atom, and add two to account for the hydrogen atoms at the ends." This was written on the board as:− " Each carbon atom has a hydrogen atom above and below it, so multiply C by 2 to give 2C. There is a hydrogen atom at each end so add 2. Combining these gives $H = 2C + 2$."

The formula for the number of bonds, $B = 3C + 1$, was discussed at greater length. Several pupils explained that C was multiplied by three because each carbon atom had three bonds (left, or right, top and bottom) and there was an extra bond on the right, or left. One pupil suggested that the bonds could be seen as three sets: all those above the carbon atoms, all those below and those to the right. The class was then asked to consider solving the problem by beginning with the fact that (as had a few pupils in the written reports) the carbon atoms on the ends had four bonds each. Several could then explain that all other carbon atoms had two hydrogen bonds and that this meant adding $2(2C - 2)$. It took longer to find an expression for the number of bonds connecting the remaining carbon atoms. The diagram for $C = 5$ was drawn on the board and the number of such bonds for $C = 1, 2, 3, 4,$ and 5 counted. Some pupils could then suggest that the required expression was $C - 3$. The total number of bonds was then found by combining these results: $C = 2 \times 4 + 2 (C - 2) + C - 3 = 3C + 1$.

There was little overt reaction to the fact that two such apparently different approaches should produce the same result. However this is considered to be an important aspect of mathematics and it is appropriate to expose pupils to the phenomenon.

Pupil Challenge

Spiked wall

The following patterns were made with matchsticks.

Copy and complete the following table.

Number of spikes	Length of wall	Number of matchsticks
s	w	m
1	1	6
2	3	14
3		
4		
5		

Try to find formulae for w and m in terms of s.

Explain how you obtained your formulae.

Explain how you can be sure they will always work.

Convince a penfriend.

This is the first of two matchstick investigations, from DIME "Number Patterns 2" (Giles, p8). They were set as homework assignments for the fourteen and fifteen year old pupils in the experimental group and so there is no introductory lesson. This has since been successfully used as a class activity with thirteen year old pupils familiar with the idea of proof. The following outline summarises a lesson with younger pupils.

Lesson Outline (30 minutes)

Spiked wall

1. Explain the task.
2. Pupils work in pairs and collate results.
3. Pupils discuss results in pairs or fours.
4. Begin class discussion – ask pupils how to find the length of the wall (w).
5. Discuss patterns and formulae/connections. Compare alternative responses.
6. Ask pupils to explain formulae/connections. Compare alternative responses.

7. Consider the number of matches – repeat 5 and 6.

8. (If appropriate) Explain the content expected in written reports – results, patterns, connections/formulae, explanations.

Pupil reports

Most pupils in the experimental group described the pattern of odd numbers for the wall length or recognised that it increased by two for each additional spike and many obtained a correct formula ($w = 2s - 1$) in terms of the number of spikes (s). One boy explained that this included -1 because multiplying by two always produced a value one more than was required. He, like more than half the pupils, also explained how the formula related to the diagrams by reference to the fact that each new spike involved adding two units of length except for the initial spike.

Although a few pupils had errors in the results about two thirds found a correct formula for the number of matches. Those who quoted $m = 8s - 2$, in some cases by reference to successive differences, were in most cases able to relate this correctly to the diagram. Multiplying by eight was because each spike pattern used eight matches and subtracting two was to account for removing the extra two matches at either beginning or end. Three pupils said, incorrectly and imprecisely, that two was subtracted "because of the spike." A few pupils related the number of matches to the wall length by the formula $m = 4w + 2$ but no-one was able to explain this version.

Robert's (able thirteen year old) report

The following report was written by an able boy as a homework assignment after the lesson outlined above.

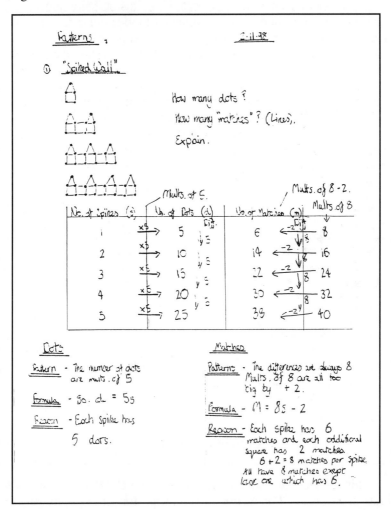

Lesson – Follow-up discussion

This lesson was with the pupils in the experimental group, who had first attempted the investigation independently for homework. At the beginning of the lesson a table of correct results, provided by pupils, was drawn on the board and both formulae in *s* derived and explained with little difficulty. As no-one was able to explain the formula in w it was converted to one in s using the substitution $w = 2s - 1$ which had already been derived and proved. It was clear that the pupils did not perceive this investigation to be too simple for them, as had been suspected. On this occasion most pupils had independently derived and explained the formulae and the class discussion was simply an opportunity to ensure that all pupils were made aware of these, and for confident pupils to explain them to their peers.

Pupil Challenge

Joined hexagons

The following patterns were made with matchsticks.
Copy and complete the table below.

Number of hexagons	Number of dots	Number of matchsticks
h	d	m
1	6	6
2	11	14
3		
4		
5		

Try to find formulae for d and m in terms of h.
Explain how you obtained your formulae.

Explain how you can be sure they will always work.

Convince a penfriend.

This second matchstick investigation from *DIME* (2, p7) was also first used as a homework assignment for the pupils in the experimental group, and has since been used as a class activity with younger pupils. Because of its similarity to "Spiked Wall" only the pupil worksheet and pupil reports are included.

Pupil reports

All pupils found a correct formula for the number of dots (d) and all but three had an adequate or good explanation, many referring to diagrams. Many also tested their formula with numerical values and seemed to appreciate the difference between this and proof. All but three quoted the expected version of the formula, $d = 5h + 1$, explaining that all hexagons (h) except the first or last required an additional five dots. The other pupils quoted, $d = 6h - (h - 1)$, and explained that if six dots were counted for every hexagon this would be one too many for all except an end.

Finding and explaining a formula for the number of matches (m) seemed to be slightly more difficult. Four pupils were unable to find a formula, one because she had miscopied the diagrams, and an additional five were unable to explain the formula they found although one of these wrote sufficient to indicate that he understood the proof but did not quite explain -2 in his formula. Most pupils quoted $m = 8h - 2$ explaining that each complete addition to the row needed eight matches except that a hexagon at one end did not have two joining matches. Two pupils quoted $m = 6h + 2(h - 1)$ explaining that each hexagon needed six matches and all but an end one also needed two joining matches. Another formulae quoted and explained well was $m = (h - 1) + 6$. One girl quoted $m = 7h + (h - 2)$ but only explained $7h$. One boy quoted, $m = 3(h - 1) + d$, and although he tested it with numerical values was unable to explain it.

Because of the success of most of the pupils in completing this work the problem was not discussed at length in the following lesson. Instead those who had succeeded were asked to explain their answers to the class and anyone who had difficulties in understanding invited to ask for further help later. No-one did and it is reasonable to suppose that the problem had been understood by all. The following explanation was written by a fourteen year old girl in a class which had only recently been introduced to the notion of proof.

Carol's "proof"

The formula for the number of dots was $6h - (h - 1)$. This is obtained from the following method. Each hexagon has six angles and on each angle is a dot.

When two hexagons are joined together one of the dots is shared i.e.

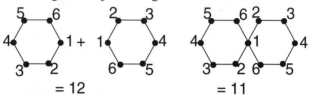

If 3 hexagons were joined two dots would be shared etc. Hence $6h - (h - 1)$ gives the number of dots.

The formula for the number of matches is $6h + 2(h - 1)$. This is obtained from the following method.

As in the previous explanation for the formula for the number of dots in a hexagon there are six sides. Each hexagon is joined to another by two matches, one at the base and another at the top i.e.

⟨ ⟩ ⟨ ⟩ = ⟨ ⟩⟨ ⟩   — = matches joined

If there were three hexagons the two outside ones had to be joined to the central hexagon by two pairs of bonds. If there were four hexagons there would be three pairs of matches acting as bonds. Hence the formula is $6h + 2(h - 1)$.

Pupil Challenge

L-shapes

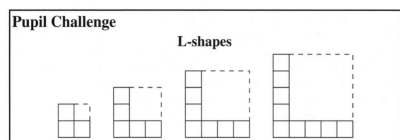

For the above pattern of L-shapes made from matches:–

1. Copy and complete the table down to $n = 6$.

Size of large square (n)	Number of small squares (s)	Perimeter of L-shape (P)	Number of matches (m)
2	3	8	10
3			
4			
5			
6			

2. Describe any patterns you see.
3. Find formulae for the following in terms of n:–
   a) the number of small squares (s);
   b) the perimeter (number of matches around the outside) of the L-shape (P).
   c) the number of matches used (m).
4. Prove that your formulae are correct by explaining how each one is connected to the diagram.

Remember – checking is not proving.
Convince a penfriend.

This investigation, also from DIME "Number Patterns 2" (Giles, p 12), includes three linear patterns at a suitable level of difficulty. It was initially used as a class activity with the experimental group at the end of the teaching programme, just before a test to assess the effect, if any, of teaching about proof. Pupils were asked to complete a table to $n = 6$ (n is the number of small squares in one arm of the L) to enable as many pupils as possible to recognise the patterns. A reminder that checking is not proof was included in the pupil worksheet.

This activity is recommended for use towards the end of this phase. A lesson outline is not included here because teachers will now be familiar with leading this type of discussion, and aware of the need to follow pupil suggestions about the various valid explanations rather then a predetermined plan. The introductory lesson will take between forty-five and sixty minutes and the follow-up discussion ten to twenty minutes.

Lesson 1 – Introduction

This lesson is described in some detail to illustrate pupil reactions as they worked on the task either independently or with others, and during a class discussion. As the pupils had undergone a teaching programme which emphasised proof they were familiar with the idea of explaining patterns but some were still finding this difficult unless the patterns were very simple. This activity includes two such patterns and one that is less obvious to find and therefore more difficult to explain.

At the beginning of the lesson pupils were given a copy of the above worksheet and told to work independently or in pairs to collect results and to begin to analyse them. During this period it was possible to talk to some pupils and listen to others. One girl was puzzling over the perimeter because she failed to recognise multiples of four. She could explain that the values increased "in steps" but, until prompted, did not observe they were of four. As soon as she realised this she was able to express the relationship as $P = 4n$. Another girl, working nearby on her own was heard to say, "O, I get it!" as she recognised the numbers of small squares were odd numbers. A third pupil who appeared to be wasting time had in fact obtained all three formulae, and was congratulated and encouraged to search for explanations.

After about fifteen minutes pupils were asked for the numerical values of the three variables and these were recorded on the board. None of them had any problems with this. They were reminded that they were not only looking for patterns and formulae but also for explanations, and told to continue the investigation. A few pupils needed help to identify patterns and this was usually achieved by examining differences in successive values as a means of finding at least part of a formula. An able boy (Tim) very quickly wrote explanations for all but the last formula and said he was trying to analyse this like the "Hydrocarbons" investigation but he was having difficulty with corner and end matches. A girl could see that the number of matches was related to $P + s$ and as she talked about it realised the relation was $m = P + s + 1$. She was slightly puzzled when asked how she could get this in terms of n but needed very little explanation before she could continue with confidence.

A class discussion of formulae and explanations was begun after a further fifteen minutes. The formula $s = 2n - 1$ was generally agreed but a boy said he had $n + n - 1$ but realised that this was the same as soon as it was written on the board above the $2n - 1$. When asked for possible explanations several pupils could offer that n was the bottom row (or side) and $n - 1$ was the other row; or that if the side were to be laid alongside the bottom row there would be a double row with one square missing.

The formula $P = 4n$ was readily obtained as most pupils had recognised multiples of four. A girl explained her method which seemed to be generally understood. She saw the shorter lines translated, match by match, to complete a square of side n with perimeter $4n$ (Diagram 1). Tim explained that he saw the end matches added on to the inside lines so that they were of length n making four lines of this length in all (Diagram 2). The rest of the class seemed satisfied with both these explanations.

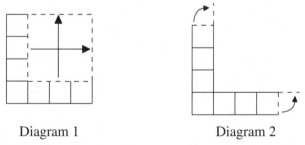

Diagram 1   Diagram 2

The last formula was more difficult but several pupils had realised that the number of matches was the same as $P + s - 1$ and a few had a formula in terms of n. The class was then asked for replacements for P and s in terms of n and the expression $6n - 2$ obtained. This was not considered in minute detail but pupils were encouraged to recognise the possibility of explaining it in several different ways. A few pupils were asked to tell the rest of the class the essence of their explanation. Tim again made the comparison with "Hydrocarbons" and said that he saw each new square as three new matches. Another had essentially the same idea but saw the bottom and side separately. They were also asked to consider the arrangement of the squares as two horizontal rows of squares each double square requiring an additional six matches.

The emphasis in this part of the discussion was on the fact that there were several equally valid ways of explaining this formula. During the last few minutes of the lesson the pupils began to write a report of the investigation and were asked to complete it for homework.

Pupil reports

All pupils obtained correct formulae and, except for one who just repeated the formulae by way of explanation, made some attempt to explain them.

Nearly half had exemplary explanations for the formula for s, and only three gave muddled responses. One partial explanation described in detail why the number of squares was $2 \times 3 - 1$ for the third stage but did not generalise the idea. Another used only diagrams but no verbal explanation. In explaining the formula for P one third were good or excellent, and a similar proportion at least partially correct. One incorrect explanation suggested that $P = 4n$ because each square is made up of four matches.

Only three pupils derived and gave good explanations for $m = 6n - 2$, but nearly half were able to explain other versions of the formula. For instance one derived $m = 3s + 1$ and explained that each new square needed three matches and one match was needed to start the pattern. Another pupil gave a good explanation of the fact that there were $4n$ matches around the outside and a slightly muddled explanation that there were $2n - 1 - 1$ matches inside the pattern and combined these to give "$6n - 2$". One pupil quoted the formula $m = P + s + 1$ but gave no explanation and another, in attempting to derive and explain a formula for m, moved the squares around and changed the total number of matches without realising it.

Lesson 2 – Follow-up discussion

Those pupils who had been able to explain the first two formulae were asked to do so to the class and all seemed to understand. The various formulae for m were written on the board and their equivalence considered. With prompting the pupils were able to replace s and P in terms of n and simplify the results. For instance one girl was able to explain that $P + s - 1$ became $4n + 2n - 1 - 1$ which could be simplified to give $6n - 2$.

The following three investigations were first used as part of a test to assess the ability of pupils, in the experimental and two control groups, to find and analyse patterns. The pupils in the experimental group had by now been exposed to proof discussions and activities for nine months. In the control groups there was no reference to proof, but one group had received specific teaching about pattern-spotting techniques. They had, for instance, been taught the method of differences.

These investigations have since been used with pupils who are familiar with the notion of proof but not competent or confident when writing proofs. Only the pupil responses in the test are described here, and some extensions suggested.

Pupil Challenge

Calendar squares

In the diagram showing the calendar for the month of May, a group of four numbers in a square has been highlighted.

MAY						
Sun	Mon	Tues	Wed	Thur	Fri	Sat
	1	2	3	4	5	6
7	8	9	10	11	12	13
14	15	16	17	18	19	20
21	22	23	24	25	26	27
28	29	30	31			

Adding diagonally opposite numbers in this square gives:–

$$15 + 23 = 38$$
and $$16 + 22 = 38$$

Repeat for other squares.

Describe what you notice about the totals.

Explain why this happens.

Convince a penfriend.

This is typical of a series of problems based on number patterns in rectangular or square arrays of integers. Although algebra is clearly the most efficient means of explaining the relationships its use is not essential. Indeed, those pupils whose facility with algebra is sufficiently well-developed, will still find value in explaining the relationships in their own words first.

Pupil responses

In the test the proof for "Calendar Squares" was successfully completed by about 60% of the pupils in each control group and by

84% of those in the experimental group. Most correct proofs were written informally, many with diagrams. A girl in one control group wrote "The totals for the diagonals are always the same because the top two numbers and the bottom two numbers have a difference of 1. The smaller number on top goes to the larger number on the bottom and vice versa." A girl in the experimental group included an algebraic explanation $x + y = (x + 1) + (y - 1)$. A girl in the second control group correctly identified the patterns but did not explain fully the essence of the problem: "There is a gap of 7 going down the table so there will always be a gap of 8 diagonally."

In interviews with some pupils the only difficulty was in explaining their thinking in writing. One girl in the experimental group said, "It was hard to explain but only in that it took a lot of explanation. It's easier to talk."

If this activity is used in the classroom pupils could investigate and explain a general rule for larger and smaller arrays of numbers, for larger squares or rectangles within the arrays, and/or the products of the numbers in the corners.

Pupil Challenge

Fenceposts

Complete the table to show the number of rails needed to build each fence.

Number of posts (p)	Number of rails (r)
1	0
2	3
3	
4	
5	
6	

Describe any patterns you see.

Write down a formula for the number of rails (r) needed for a fence with p posts.

Explain how the number of rails is connected to the number of posts.

Explain why the formula always works.

Convince a penfriend.

This task, on building a fence, was included in the test as an example similar to several problems included in the teaching programme for the experimental group.

Pupil responses

The majority of pupils, from both experimental and control groups, correctly observed multiples of three but a significant minority described other patterns. Some noticed that the number of rails could be found by doubling the number of posts and adding the "next number", and others that adding the next odd number to the number of posts gave the number of rails.

The control groups were both significantly different from the experimental group with respect to recognising the pattern, but not from each other. Since the experimental group was the only one exposed to explaining patterns it seems likely that this exposure enhanced their ability to recognise patterns. The similar performances of pupils in the two control groups was surprising because one group had been taught some techniques for pattern-spotting. This had not enhanced their mean group performance in this question, possibly because the gains of some pupils were offset by the losses of others.

The response of a girl in this group is an illustration of how concentration on finding differences may have inhibited further progress. She recognised that each post added three more rails, and in describing how to get the number of rails from the number of posts she wrote "If you find out the difference of the number of posts and the number of rails then find out the difference of the difference of the posts and rails you will find that the difference is two each time. Each time if you add two on to the difference then add the number of posts you will get the number of rails." She had correctly identified a property of the number pattern (since $r = 3p - 3$, then $r - p = 2p - 3$ and successive differences of these values are always two) but was unable to use it to relate the two variables with a formula. Four other girls in the group had adopted a similar approach and been unable to find a formula. These reactions corroborate Kerslake's (1994) assertion that concentration on pattern-spotting can preclude understanding mathematics, and justify Gardiner's view (1993) that pupils should be encouraged to search for underlying structures rather than superficial patterns.

Two examples of the sixteen correct explanations from the experimental group were:– "For every post you add three rails but you don't have three rails where there is no post at the end and so you take away three rails" (for $r = 3p - 3$) and "There are three rails to every post ($\times 3$) (*sic*) and there must be a spare rail at the end to close off the other rails, but this doesn't have any rails of its own so, $(p - 1)$ (*sic*)" (for $r = 3(p - 1)$). A girl gave a longer explanation which included "A fence cannot be made with only one post, therefore for one post no rails are needed. A fence needs at least 2 posts. But once you have a post, for every additional post the fence can be extended by 3 rails and once you have the first post the fence can be continuously extended."

There were only seven correct explanations out of forty-eight from both control groups. A girl wrote, "There are 3 rails for each post, (excluding the first post) but a 3 has to be deducted to account for the first post" (for $r = 3p - 3$) and a boy wrote, "For every post added 3 rails are needed except for 1 post, because there is no other end for the rails to go," to explain $r = 3(p - 1)$. A girl explained $r = 3p - 3$ by writing, "You always need one less set of 3 rails than the number of posts." There were eight partially correct answers from pupils in the control groups, including "No matter how many posts you put down the number of rails needed will always increase by 3 for each post" and "You need to minus 3 because one post hasn't any rails." A few pupils (none from the experimental group) quoted special cases as proof, e.g.. "You can do it for 1; you can do it for 10; you can do it for 100; and it will always work"; " All the numbers always work out OK (*sic*)"; and "No matter how many posts there are it will always give the correct amount (*sic*) of rails, i.e. $3 \times 20 - 3 = 57$." These examples support the view of Bell et al (1983) that often pupils use particular cases as if they were general. The fact that instances of this were only given by pupils in the control groups tends to corroborate Bell's further suggestion (1983) that appreciating the difference between checking and proving is sensitive to teaching.

Of the eight pupils in the experimental group who were interviewed about this question six had full correct answers and had found the question very straightforward. A girl who had an error in the table and had left the question unfinished had written, "It goes up by three," and said in the interview, "It takes me a long time to figure it out. I tried times by (*sic*) two and add one, and times by two and add two. .... I just tried things!" She had clearly not connected the relationship between numbers in the table to the structure of the pattern on this occasion.

> # Pupil Challenge
> ## Multiplying consecutive integers
> {9, 10, 11, 12, 13} is a set of five consecutive integers.
> (a) How many multiples of i) 2   ii) 3   iii) 4   iv) 5 are there?
> (b) What is the maximum number of multiples of i) 2   ii) 3   iii) 4
> iv) 5 in any set of five consecutive integers?
> (c) 2 × 3 × 4 = 24   is a product (multiplication) of three consecutive integers.
>   i)   Work out the product of three other consecutive integers.
>   ii) Repeat until you see a pattern.
>   iii) What appears to be true every time?
>   iv) Explain why this will always happen when three consecutive integers are multiplied.
> ## Convince a penfriend.

Some teachers may consider this to be more appropriate for the next phase, when pupils are likely to be competent in their use of algebra. However, an algebraic approach is not the best proof for the result, and confidence in algebra might be said to be a disadvantage! This seemed to be the case for the student teachers described by Perks and Prestage (1995), who had difficulty in explaining this property despite their facility with algebra.

The first part of the question was intended to focus the pupils' minds on the idea of multiples so that this important part of the proof was "ready to hand". To tell the pupils to use multiples of two and three in the main part of the question would lose an important aspect of the creation of a proof. An alternative starting point for analysing this property is to consider the product of two consecutive integers as equivalent to the product of an odd and an even number.

Pupil responses

In the experimental group one girl recognised multiples of six, a boy identified two and three as factors, and nine were able to identify multiples of two or three. Four pupils in the control group, which had received no specific instruction or practice in patterns, also identified multiples of two or three. Two pupils in the control group which had been taught techniques for pattern-spotting recognised multiples of two and six noticed multiples of six. Four of these identified the importance of six by using the method of differences but made no reference to factors or multiples. A girl in this group wrote "If you find the differences of the differences, the differences of these seem to be 6," but did not continue. These are further examples of the fact that knowledge of this particular technique may inhibit progress, which provides additional support to Gardiner (1993) and Kerslake (1994).

There were no acceptable proofs for this question and only eight pupils (four in the experimental group and four in the control groups) had partial explanations. All but one of these realised that a set of three consecutive numbers would include at least one even number, making the product even. One wrote, "This (multiples of two) will always happen because there is at least one multiple of 2 in every set of (three) consecutive integers and so it will always be divisible by two and be an even number." These responses suggest that their authors had no thought of using algebra to explain the pattern, and so the stumbling block here is different from that of the PGCE students described by Perks and Prestage (1995).

During the interviews about this question it was clear that all interviewees were familiar with multiples but three had not found the maximum number of multiples. However, they were able to do this when multiples of (2,3,4,5) were considered separately, and different sets of consecutive integers examined. One girl said that she had not appreciated the connection between the first and second parts of the test question. The best written answer had been from a boy who had spent so long on this question that he did not attempt any further questions in the test. He had worked out several examples, divided them by two and three separately, but had not combined these ideas. During the interview he was able to recognise that his results were all multiples of six and his initial explanation was, "It's something to do with the number of numbers." He was readily led to a full understanding of the structure of the problem, as was another boy who recognised the presence of multiples of three in the test and suggested in the interview that it was connected with the "increasing gaps". These two were on the verge of understanding the problem unaided, unlike all other interviewees who had made little progress in the written test and needed much more guidance to an appreciation and explanation of the presence of multiples of six. Typical comments about this question were:– " I spent a long time on this" and "I didn't really understand it.

Despite these pupil difficulties subsequent class discussions suggest that this is a valid property to discuss during this phase, even though significant teacher direction may be needed to enable pupils to recognise multiples of six. In the experience of the author, when pupils are asked to investigate this problem most observe even numbers, one or two recognise multiples of three, one or two multiples of six, and one or two that the third successive differences are always six. Although it is rare for a pupil to be able to offer a full explanation of the property initially, it is usually possible to elicit responses from pupils so that a "class proof" is constructed. This will be based on the fact that any set of three consecutive integers includes at least one multiple of two and one multiple of three and that therefore the product is a multiple of six.

Some textbooks, and other sources, include examples of patterns for investigation but pupils cannot always explain the results obtained. If the teacher encourages pupils to look for explanations such patterns provide a useful source of proof activities. The following two suggestions are typical of those frequently used in classrooms. A pupil worksheet and possible explanations of patterns are included here.

Pupil Challenge

Painted cubes

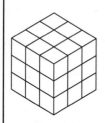

A cube is made from some small cubes.

It is dipped in a tin of paint so that the outside is coloured.

How many small cubes have no paint on?

How many small cubes have one face painted?

How many small cubes have two faces painted?

How many small cubes have three faces painted?

Investigate for different sized cubes.

What is the total number of small cubes?

Put your results in a table.

Size of cube	Number of small cubes with ... painted				Total
	0 faces	1 face	2 faces	3 faces	
1 × 1					
2 × 2					
3 × 3					

Look for patterns.

Explain how they are connected to the cubes.

Try to use algebra.

Convince a penfriend.

This investigation provides an example of a proof in three-dimensional space. If pupils are provided with unit cubes, and/or encouraged to draw diagrams, they are able to obtain results and identify some patterns unaided. Again the use of algebra is helpful here, but is not an essential prerequisite to describing the four patterns and explaining them. These can be summarised as follows:–

i)   there are always eight "corner" cubes with three faces painted because all cubes have eight corners;

ii)   the number of "edge" cubes with two faces painted – $12(n-2)$ – is a multiple of twelve because there are twelve edges and a multiple of two less than n (or cube size) because the corners on the edges have already been counted;

iii)   the number of "face" cubes with one face painted – $6(n - 2)^2$ –
is a multiple of six because a cube has six faces and a multiple
of the square of two less than n because outer cubes on each
square face have already been counted;

iv)   the number of "inner" cubes with no paint on – $(n - 2)^3$ – is the
cube of two less than n as they are the remaining cubes when
the outer layer is removed.

Pupil Challenge

Frogs

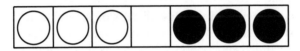

It is helpful to draw a row of squares for this game.

Two sets of counters of different colours are used for frogs.

They are placed in a row, with a space between each set, as shown
above.

The object of the game is for the black and white counters to
change places.

Only the following moves are allowed:–

> a slide into an empty space,
>
> a jump over a counter of a different colour.

Also white counters can only be moved to the right and black
counters to the left.

What is the least number of moves needed for three counters on
each side to change places?

Investigate for different numbers of counters.

Try to find connections between numbers of moves and numbers of
counters.

Look for patterns.

Try to explain them.

Use algebra if you can.

Convince a penfriend.

This investigation can be introduced by replacing the counters with pupils at the front of the class. Time should then be allowed for pupils to discover how to move counters and obtain least numbers of moves.

Once pupils have recorded the minimum number of moves (m in classes where algebra is to be used) for up to four or five counters on each side, many can observe that m increases by the addition of consecutive odd numbers as n (number of counters on one side) increases by one. Some can identify a form of the relationship $m = n(n + 2)$, but do not necessarily express this algebraically. Pupils are rarely able to explain these patterns spontaneously but they can usually be led to an understanding of the structure through class discussion, and then some are able to write their explanations.

The first objective of the class discussion should be to try to elicit the suggestion that the types of moves, namely slides and jumps, should be recorded separately. When this is done pupils can observe even numbers and square numbers, but are still unable to explain why. If pupils are asked why slides are necessary it is possible they may realise that it is to pass the space. If not they should be given time to move counters again until they see this connection. The teacher will recommend that they use two or three counters on each side as small but "representative" numbers. Class discussion should lead to general agreement that every counter slides once and so the number of slides is equal to the total number of counters, i.e. $2n$.

Similar consideration of jumps usually elicits the suggestion that each counter on one side jumps (or is jumped over by) each counter on the other side, creating n^2 jumps. If pupils have been recording the actual moves in some way, such as writing S and J for slides and jumps in lists of moves for different numbers of counters, or illustrating the positions of the counters after each move, then the symmetry in the formula can be compared with the symmetry observable in the patterns of moves.

Some pupils may extend the investigation by considering the problem for unequal numbers of counters on each side, say n and p. In this case the number of slides is $n + p$ and the number of jumps is np giving minimum number of moves as $(n + p) + np$.

This last proof activity is included as an example of a proof by exhaustion.

Pupil Challenge

Partitioning

Three objects can be partitioned in three ways:–

2 sets	a set of 2 objects and then a set of 1object	** *
	a set of 1 object and then a set of 2 objects	* **
3 sets	each of 1 object	* * *

In how many ways can a) four objects
                                        b) five objects   be partitioned?

Convince a penfriend that you have examined all possibilities.

Although essentially similar to "Dot-to-dot Triangles" in Phase 1 there are more cases to consider, and pupils are encouraged to write a proof. It may be considered necessary to remind pupils of the need for systematic analysis of all possible cases before they attempt this task. Pupils could work in pairs or individually, or the task could be completed through class discussion.

During this phase such a proof by exhaustion, which is appropriate because there is a relatively small number of cases to consider, can be usefully contrasted with the need for a generalised proof when the number of cases is large or infinite, e.g. to establish that the angle sum for any triangle is 180°, or that the area of any triangle is ½ (base × height). Reference has already been made (Chapter 1) to the possibility of proof by exhaustion that there are 256 squares on an 8 × 8 chessboard.

"Not proof"

As at Phase 1, it is still not appropriate to consider a formal definition of proof, but an appreciation of its essence can be enhanced by the following investigation and fallacies.

The pattern which results from some investigations is apparently correct for the first few terms of a sequence, but not thereafter. Slomson (1996) claims that such examples are necessary to persuade pupils of the need for proof. In "Regions in a Circle" the expression 2^{n-1}, apparently true up to $n = 5$, does not give the number of regions for n dots thereafter. Thus substituting $n > 5$ forms a proof by counter-example. Examining this problem highlights the need, not only to check formulae carefully with particular examples, but also to justify formulae by reference to the original problem. The correct formula is not easily derivable for most pupils of this age and ability and so is unlikely to be attempted. Instead it should be quoted, with reference to the existence of a proof. Pupils interested in deriving it should be shown a copy of a proof (e.g.. Beevers, 1994, p 10).

Fallacies also serve to reinforce the need to check all conjectures. Ball (1956, p 41) refers to fallacies as "instances of demonstrations leading to ..... results which are obviously impossible". Northrop begins a chapter (1961, p 80) on "Algebraical Fallacies" by a reminder that, although some paradoxes appear to be false but are in fact true, others which appear to be true are in fact false, and derive from a fallacious argument. The five elementary fallacies in this section include three which are essentially algebraic, one spatial, and one based on number.

The next worksheet was given to the pupils in the experimental group as a homework assignment. It is, of course, debatable whether pupils should think about the problem in isolation at home, or discuss their ideas with their peers in a class activity. The pupils in the experimental group were asked to provide a written report so that the teacher could analyse their thinking. On other occasions class discussions have been successfully used.

Pupil Challenge

Regions in a circle

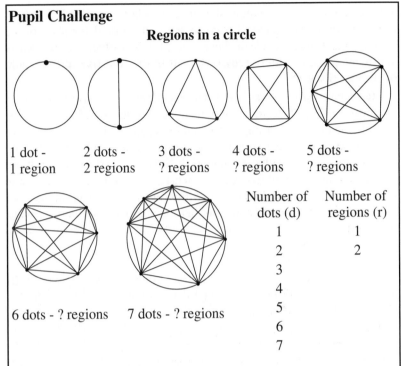

| 1 dot - | 2 dots - | 3 dots - | 4 dots - | 5 dots - |
| 1 region | 2 regions | ? regions | ? regions | ? regions |

6 dots - ? regions   7 dots - ? regions

Number of dots (d)	Number of regions (r)
1	1
2	2
3	
4	
5	
6	
7	

Spend about 20 minutes on questions 1 and 2.

1. Complete the table on the right only up to $d = 5$.
2. a) Can you suggest a suitable formula connecting d and r?
   b) Does it work for $d = 6$ and $d = 7$?

Spend about 10 minutes on question 3.

3. Explain your formula if you found one and/or describe your thinking about the problem.

Pupil reports

The reports written by pupils in the experimental group showed that about one third of the pupils used the idea of doubling the previous value to complete the table for $d = 6$ and $d = 7$ but did not appear to have checked the values by counting. One pupil correctly counted the number of regions for $d = 6$ and $d = 7$ and then crossed out his answers to fit the pattern of doubling that he recognised. He clearly had more faith in a formula than in his ability to count! Even the only pupil who quoted the formula $r = 2^{d-1}$

(correct up to $d = 5$) which, she said, "Came to me just by looking at the results," continued "I tried to see if it worked for $d = 6$ and $d = 7$ and it did." Each of these, and probably others, were clearly confident that the pattern they observed in the first five terms would be universally true.

One pupil report included an excellent description of failed attempts to find a formula and listed differences and squaring as ideas he had tried. This pupil was making progress in a willingness to analyse a problem, and to express ideas in words. The best reports were from two girls. One explained "I thought I had found a pattern to find the next r. It is to double. It worked for up to $d = 5$ but then it failed." Another wrote "For 1 to 5 the formula is $2r$ i.e. the number of regions for the number of dots before $\times$ 2. But this doesn't work for 6 and 7."

Lesson – Follow-up discussion

During subsequent class discussion it became clear to all pupils that the proposed formula did not fit the counted regions for higher values of d. The importance of justifying formulae was stressed and seemed to be appreciated by the pupils. It was explained that, although the initial attempt at a formula had been incorrect, it was reasonable to suppose that such a formula existed but that it was complex and they were not expected to find or prove it. There was obvious relief about this but several pupils were interested to know what it was. A copy was offered to anyone who was interested, and one boy and one girl accepted.

Pupil responses in another class discussion

On a more recent occasion some very able fourteen year old pupils were given the pupil worksheet about fifteen minutes before the end of a lesson. They were told to work in pairs to collect results for up to five dots, and to look for patterns. When most had completed this, and some had examined the remaining diagrams, the results for up to five dots were tabulated on the board. Then the pattern of doubling was observed and the results recorded as powers of two (recognised by a pupil). The formula $r = 2^{d-1}$ was suggested by a pupil. There was general acceptance of this, even by some pupils who claimed to have counted the number of regions for six dots.

They were then told to count carefully the number of regions in the remaining diagrams to confirm their predictions. There was some consternation but after a few minutes a girl, who had numbered all the regions, was confident enough to claim that there were thirty-one and so the formula was incorrect. Other pupils then agreed. On this occasion pupils were not asked for a written report and the lesson concluded by writing one version of the correct formula on the board, and a warning of the need to prove all apparent formulae.

Fallacies

In algebra

1) A "proof" that $2 = 1$ (Ball, p 41 and Northrop, p 85)

Let	$a = b$
then multiplying by a	$a^2 = ab$
subtracting b^2	$a^2 - b^2 = ab - b^2$
factorising	$(a + b)(a - b) = b(a - b)$
dividing by $(a - b)$	$a + b = b$
substituting for a	$2b = b$
dividing by b	$2 = 1$

Although not all pupils will be able to identify the error of dividing by zero ($a - b = 0$) many will understand the argument and appreciate the error when it is shown to them.

2) Two "proofs" that $-1 = 1$ ((a) Ball, p 42 and (b) Northrop, p 96)

(a) $\sqrt{a} \times \sqrt{b} = \sqrt{ab}$

$$\sqrt{-1} \times \sqrt{-1} = \sqrt{(-1)(-1)}$$

$$\sqrt{(-1)^2} = \sqrt{1}$$

$$-1 = 1$$

(b) $\sqrt{(-1)} = \sqrt{(-1)}$

$$\sqrt{\frac{1}{-1}} = \sqrt{\frac{-1}{1}}$$

$$\frac{\sqrt{1}}{\sqrt{-1}} = \frac{\sqrt{-1}}{\sqrt{1}}$$

$$\sqrt{1} \times \sqrt{1} = \sqrt{(-1)} \times \sqrt{(-1)}$$

$$1 = -1$$

Again, pupils are unlikely to recognise the flaw in these arguments, namely ignoring the negative square root, but are capable of appreciating this when it is pointed out to them.

A square dissection

This dissection (Ball, p 85) is an excellent illustration of the danger of relying on purely visual information, and is particularly useful as a justification for rejecting Perigal's dissection as a proof of Pythagoras' theorem.

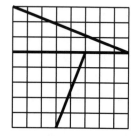

Superficial inspection suggests that the four pieces which form a square of area sixty-four square units (8 × 8) can be rearranged to form a rectangle of area sixty-five square units (5 × 13). Closer inspection reveals that what appears to be a straight line AB is in fact a parallelogram with acute angle less than 1¼° ($\tan^{-1}\frac{2}{5} - \tan^{-1}\frac{5}{8}$). Although this is undetectable by measuring and therefore unlikely to be discovered by pupils, they are likely to appreciate that AB cannot be straight because the two segments are of different gradients (slopes if gradient is an unfamiliar term).

Ancestors

In this last fallacy, described by Northrop (1961, p 31) it is reasonable to expect that some pupils will be able to detect the error and so it might be appropriate for them to discuss this in small groups before a class discussion. The essence of the fallacy is as follow:–

For each generation the number of ancestors doubles, e.g. you have 2 parents, 4 grandparents, and 8 great grandparents. So n generations ago you had 2^n ancestors. Since each generation is about 20 years, 600 years, or 30 generations, ago you, and everyone else alive had 2^{30} = 1 040 400 ancestors. Someone used this argument to "prove" that the population was more than 1 000 000 times larger 600 years ago than it is today. Where is the flaw in the "proof"?

Optional assessment task

Pupils who have written reports on the proof activities suggested in this chapter could take written assessment. Clearly the context in which proof is expected should be similar to that previously experienced through the pattern investigations. Although these patterns are slightly more complex than in the previous chapter most of the explanations have related to a concrete situation and/or a diagram. A suitable task for independent assessment is essentially a two dimensional variation of the "Painted Cubes" investigation and is described in the pupil worksheet below.

Pupil Challenge

Windows

corner
panes

A 3 by 3 window

edge
panes

uses 4 corner panes

4 edge panes

centre
panes

and 1 centre pane

Investigate for other sizes of windows.

Tabulate your results as shown below:–

	Size of window	Number of corner panes	Number of edge panes	Number of centre panes	Total number of panes
	1×1				
Square	2×2				
windows	3×3	4	4	1	9
	$n \times n$				
Rectangular					
windows	$n \times m$				

Describe any patterns you see.

Find formulae where appropriate.

Prove that your formulae are correct by explaining how each one is connected to a window.

Convince a penfriend.

Most pupils are able to identify and explain at least one pattern for square windows, and the most able can derive and explain correct formulae for rectangular windows of any size. If the only aim of the assessment is to provide pupils with a context in which they can exhibit their ability to write proofs of patterns, then the patterns within the problem need prior discussion. However, there is little value in testing proof in isolation. It is preferable for pupils to identify the patterns, so providing an option for assessing their abilities to search for and describe increasingly complex patterns.

Pupils will only be in a position to demonstrate their ability to prove if they can first identify the patterns. However, pupils learning to prove at these levels are highly likely to identify the patterns in square windows. The first might be considered trivial (constant 4) but is included so that all pupils have at least one opportunity to prove. The remaining patterns range from a linear relationship, through a square, to a two variable relationship, thus providing the most able with a suitable context for proof. Although the task provides an opportunity to assess abilities other than that to prove, only the marking with respect to its primary aim is described here.

There are two different ways of marking pupils responses with respect to ability to prove. If the award of a Proof Level is deemed to be sufficient then it is appropriate to award Proof Level 3 to any pupil who can explain that there are four "corner" panes for all windows because squares and rectangles have four corners, as such pupils demonstrate that they understand the generalised nature of proof. Proof Level 4 can be awarded to pupils who can fully explain at least one of the following patterns, in similar or equivalent terms:–

i)   there are $4(n - 2)$, or equivalent, "edge" panes for square windows because squares have four identical sides, and the corners along each have already been counted;

ii)   there are $(n - 2)^2$ "inner" panes for square windows because removing the outer "edge" and "corner" panes creates a square two sizes smaller than the original;

iii) there are $2(n + 2) + 2(m - 2)$ "edge" panes for a rectangular window $\times m$ because removing "corner" panes leaves $n - 2$ "edge" panes top and bottom, and $m - 2$" along left and right sides;

iv)   there are $(n - 2) \times (m - 2)$ "inner" panes because removing the outer "edge" and "corner" panes creates an inner rectangle two sizes smaller than the original.

It is possible that some very able pupils, who produce full correct explanations for all patterns, might be at Proof Level 5. However this assessment does not provide sufficient evidence to justify awarding this level since it only requires that pupils can prove in the context of explaining the structure of a visual pattern.

It is also possible to obtain a score for the assessment. Criterion-referencing is not the best means of doing this. There are the difficulties in predicting exactly how pupils explain their thinking, and in judging the equivalence of two alternative statements. In the opinion of the author a simple three-point scale can be used:–

2 for a clear, well-expressed, correct argument,

1 for any response with an element of correct reasoning,

0 for a a totally incorrect/illogical explanation.

For example, in (i) above, a pupil who clearly explains the connection between the factor/multiple of four and the fact that all squares have four equal sides would score two points, whereas a pupil who wrote, "There is always a factor of four because the windows are square" would only be awarded one point. A pupil who explained completely why the other factor is a multiple of $n - 2$ would similarly be awarded two points and one who explained that two is subtracted "because of the corners" would only score one point.

In a recent article in "Mathematics in Schools" (September, 1999) Hoyles and Healy used a four point scale to describe pupils' ability to explain that the addition of two odd numbers is an even number. A response with some relevant information but no deduction was awarded one point, partial proofs two, and complete proofs three points. Some teachers may prefer this option.

Conclusion

Although most of the lessons and homework assignments described in this chapter involved able fourteen and fifteen year old pupils they will be appropriate for older pupils of average ability and for some very able younger pupils. It may be necessary to reduce the emphasis on algebra, but this will not devalue the proof content of the activities as algebra is not an essential aspect of learning to prove. Teachers might also decide to abandon written reports in some cases, and possibly provide pupils with specimen reports.

The pattern-proof activities described have attempted to engage pupils in identifying patterns in a variety of contexts, working mainly independently or in small groups, and then to involve them in class discussions to arrive at explanations of the patterns. Finally, pupils have been encouraged to write informal proofs of patterns with an increasing degree of independence.

In addition to proving patterns every opportunity has been taken to justify all other mathematics in general terms whenever possible. Sometimes the proof was too difficult and particular cases used to demonstrate the truth of the ideas. When the latter have been necessary this has been admitted to pupils and the difference between generalised proof for all cases, and using a particular case to demonstrate likelihood of truth for all cases, has been repeated. In geometry pupils have been shown diagrammatic proofs with limited use of mathematical language and symbols. Only very able pupils can construct their own proofs in this domain.

At the end of this phase many pupils are able to write proofs of simple patterns independently and are thus at Proof Level 4. Some pupils understand verbal proofs in geometry and algebra but, except for the most able, cannot write these independently and so have not attained Proof Level 5.

CHAPTER 4

Phase 3 – Improving proof skills

Pupils in this last phase are secure in their knowledge and understanding of the generalised nature of proof, and their ability to write short proofs. In Proof Discussions they are exposed to traditional proofs in algebra and geometry. Proof Activities lead to pupils writing their own proofs of the results of more complex investigations. Pupils become familiar with some of the language of proof and can use a wider repertoire of proof methods. They are thus progressing –

towards formal proof.

Introduction

Pupils who acquire competence in writing proofs before examinations at sixteen are likely to benefit from some of the Proof Discussions and Proof Activities described in this chapter.

During this phase pupils are exposed to a wider range of proof types and contexts, and to more complex proofs, so that they can broaden and deepen their understanding of proof *per se*. They also practise creating a wider variety of proofs. Those who succeed in this will have attained Proof Level 5. It is also hoped that pupils acquire a deeper understanding of proof as an integral part of mathematics, and become conscious of the "wholeness" or unity of mathematics as opposed to an apparent discreteness which might be inferred from the approach in some current mathematics courses.

This chapter is structured in a similar way to Chapter 3 in that some guidance is offered on leading proof discussions of mathematical properties and then some "investigate – prove" activities are described. For the discussions proofs are provided instead of lesson outlines, and for two proof activities there are detailed and outline lesson plans. Some of the lessons described involved the pupils in the experimental group towards the end of the research teaching programme. Other lessons involved very able (top 10% of the ability range for mathematics) fifteen and sixteen year old pupils. Additionally some proof activities are described through responses in written tests and individual interviews involving pupils in both experimental and control groups. Finally, there are two short sections – one with examples of "Not Proof" and one with some suggestions for assessment.

The programme of study described in this chapter includes proofs of more unusual and more complex patterns and of more difficult mathematical concepts. It also seeks to re-emphasise the danger of assuming a conjecture is true, to raise the awareness that more than one proof may exist, and to compare different proofs of the same property. Pupils are exposed to some Euclidean geometry but this comes labelled with a large "Handle with Care" notice! It is important to attempt to develop these proofs through class discussion, accompanied by the development of a written proof, or its equivalent in diagrams, on the board. Although copying from the board (after the discussion has ended) is probably not a major obstacle at this stage, printed versions might be preferable. There should be no requirement that pupils rote learn such proofs.

Proof Discussions

The mathematics appropriate for pupils of an age and ability to appreciate some of the finer points of proof is mainly included at Levels 9 and 10 of the (English) National Curriculum, which are studied by pupils hoping to attain high grades in GCSE examinations. This section includes class discussions about some geometry proofs, and a variety of proof types in number, algebra, mensuration, and trigonometry. The geometry proofs are mainly formal deductive, but one uses proof by contradiction. Two of the deductive proofs are presented in a diagrammatic form in addition to the verbal-algebraic form. The proofs during this phase are slightly longer and more formal than previously and so proof discussions should be supported by a written summary and diagrams on the board or overhead projector. Animated diagrams in geometry created with appropriate computer technology, or calculators like the (Texas) TI-93, could be used for some theorems.

The style of the written proofs presented to pupils during this phase includes use of some of the formal language of mathematics such as theorem as opposed to fact, and mathematical symbols such as those for equivalence and "because".

Number

Square roots

A tempting conjecture is suggested by the following results:

$$\sqrt{2\,025} = 45 = 20 + 25, \ \sqrt{3\,025} = 55 = 30 + 25$$

$$\sqrt{9\,801} = 99 = 98 + 1.$$

Many pupils are likely to agree with a similar statement such as $\sqrt{4\,025} = 65 = 40 + 25$ until the insecurity of the assumption is challenged and thence the need for proof established. This is achieved by simply checking and finding that 65^2 is not $4\,025$ ($65^2 = 4225$), thus providing a counter-example.

Fermat numbers

A more challenging property of numbers, which can also be proved by reference to a counter-example, and which will interest some pupils, is the discovery by Fermat in 1640 that numbers of the form $2^{2^n} + 1$ seemed to be prime. This is true for $n = 0$, 1, 2, 3 and 4 but Fermat later began to doubt the truth of the generalisation. However it was not until 1732 that Euler discovered that the sixth Fermat number, $2^{2^6} + 1$ (= 4 294 967 297), can be expressed as 641 × 6 700 417 and is therefore not prime. This example is sufficient to disprove Fermat's initial claim that all such numbers are prime. In fact the seventh Fermat number was factorised in 1880 (by Landry), and the eighth and ninth were factorised in 1971 and 1990 respectively, with the aid of computers. This last discovery involved Internet communication between mathematicians working on powerful computers for about two months (Devlin, 1998, p 22). They have shown that the Fermat numbers up to the twenty-fourth, and some others, are composite. Mathematicians conjecture, but have not proved, that all Fermat numbers after the fifth are not prime.

Some pupils may be inspired to become interested in other mathematics by such snippets of the history of number theory, and the challenge of an unproved conjecture. It was the challenge of the more famous claim of Fermat (his "Last" theorem), that $x^n + y^n = z^n$ has no integer solutions for $n > 2$, which motivated Andrew Wiles' interest in mathematics and led to him being the first mathematician to prove Fermat's Last Theorem in 1995 (Singh, 1997).

Some pupils might also be interested in considering whether computer proofs should be accepted as proofs. Computers can be used to consider very many special cases, and/or select random special cases for testing a conjecture. Whether or not this is equivalent to proof by a logical argument is still debated in the mathematical community. Since some pupils at this level may join the mathematical community it would seem appropriate that they should be exposed to the debate.

Irrational numbers

The ability to distinguish between rational and irrational numbers is included at Level 9 of the (English) National Curriculum. It is possible to fulfil this requirement by defining rational numbers and then showing pupils some worked examples before they attempt similar questions on their own. This is an incomplete treatment without proof. The proof, by contradiction, that the square root of two is irrational appeals to some pupils because of the unusual style of reasoning. During the development of the following proof with able (10th to 25th percentile of mathematical ability range) pupils many were willing and able to make constructive suggestions.

Assume $\sqrt{2}$ is rational .

i.e. $\sqrt{2} = \dfrac{a}{b}$ where a and b are integers with no common factors

$\therefore 2 = \dfrac{a^2}{b^2}$ (squaring)

$\therefore a^2 = 2b^2$ $\left(\times b^2\right)$

$\therefore a^2$ is even .

$\therefore a$ is even.

Let $a = 2p$ where p is an integer.

$\therefore a^2 = (2p)^2 = 4p^2$

$\therefore 4p^2 = 2b^2$

$\therefore b^2 = 2p^2$ $(\div 2)$

$\therefore b$ is even.

Thus both a and b are even.

$\therefore a$ and b have a common factor of 2.

This contradicts the initial assumption.

$\therefore \sqrt{2}$ is not rational.

Pupils are often told that π is an irrational number. Its decimal value, like that of other irrational numbers, is infinite but not recurring. One boy in the author's class was not persuaded of the claim simply on this evidence. He wanted to know how he could be sure that the decimal never ended. The fact that no-one had found its last digit did not persuade him! He clearly had a sound understanding of mathematical proof! At the beginning of the next lesson he was given a copy of a proof by Lyn (1995, Microsoft Internet Explorer) and reassured that he was not expected to understand all the details. However he and others in the class would benefit by seeing some advanced mathematics.

The teacher offered a partial proof based on accepting that if $\tan x$ is rational then x is irrational. The converse of this was proved by Lambert (see Ball, 1956, Ch. XII for a history of the irrationality of π). Pupils know that $\tan \pi/4 = 1$. So $\pi/4$ and therefore π are irrational. Although this is not completely correct in that it assumes the converse of a theorem is also true it served the purpose of providing reassurance that the irrationality of π had been proved.

Algebra

Algebraic manipulation, particularly solution of equations, consists of elements of proof, namely logical generalised argument and use of mathematical symbols. If pupils are encouraged to write full solutions rather than allowed to produce partial solutions, they are gaining valuable experience in proving.

Binomial products

During this phase the diagrammatic proofs (Chapter 3) for the relationships $(x + y)^2 = x^2 + 2xy + y^2$, and $x^2 - y^2 = (x + y)(x - y)$ could be extended to include the expansion of $(x - y)^2$ and the expansion of $(x + y)(x - y)$. Discussion of these proofs, in addition to the purely algebraic equivalents, is of value for all pupils at this level inasmuch as it is further evidence of the existence of different, but equally valid, proofs for the same property. The fact that in each case the factorisation and expansion are mutually converse could lead to an appreciation of the equivalence of the two expressions as examples of algebraic identities.

Quadratic equations

When teaching the more difficult techniques for solving quadratic equations it is important to justify each method of solution before it is used. One modern text book quotes and then uses the formula $x = \left(-b \pm \sqrt{b^2 - 4ac}\right)/2a$ for solving quadratic equations before showing solutions by completing the square. This is highly unsatisfactory for pupils who have come to expect proofs. The method of completing the square should be developed through increasingly complex equations, such as $x^2 = 9$, $x^2 + 4 = 13$, $(x + 2)^2 = 9$, $x^2 + 4x + 4 = 9$, $x^2 + 4x + 3 = 8$. Once pupils have practised using this method a generalisation will develop the quadratic formula through class discussion. Pupils will still need to practise using this formula until they can use it correctly.

Algebraic proofs by counter-example

In discussion about the two relationships $\sqrt{x} < x$ and $n^2 > 2n$ pupils are unlikely to have any difficulty in realising the limited truth of each and in offering possible counter-examples. It is better if pupils can deduce the range of values for which they are true and false, but the sufficiency of one counter-example should be emphasised.

Areas and volumes

Sectors and segments

During Proof Phase 2 pupils have been introduced to a definition of π and then deduced a formula for the circumference of a circle (Chapter 3). The formula for the area has been established by dissecting of a circle into many, small sectors re-arranged to form approximate rectilinear shapes; and also by forming a circular spiral of very thin string. Proofs are not available until pupils have been introduced to calculus, but it is possible to improve on the Phase 2 dissection proofs by an increased emphasis on the concept of infinity and the need to consider a circle as infinitely many infinitely small sectors.

Once the basic formulae for circles are remembered and understood, those for sectors are readily established through class discussion. Thinking of semi-circles and quadrants as known fractions of a circle readily leads to an understanding that their arc length and area are a half and a quarter, respectively, of the circumference and area of a circle. It is then necessary to establish that, for a fixed radius, both the arc length and area of a sector are both directly proportional to the angle at the centre, say $x°$; and thence that the relevant fraction for such a sector is $x/360$. Whether pupils can then deduce how to find the area of a segment depends on their knowledge of trigonometry. The basic trigonometrical ratios and other related ideas are discussed later in this chapter.

Geometry

Traditionally, Euclidean geometry was the main medium through which elements of proof were introduced to pupils. Partly because of the difficulties some pupils experienced, possibly due to an unwise emphasis on rote learning, and partly as a result of the introduction of transformation geometry, Euclidean proofs ceased to be taught in most British schools. They are re-introduced here for able pupils with the emphasis on developing the proofs through class discussion.

Isosceles triangles

Pupils are likely to know that isosceles triangles have two equal sides and two equal angles. During this phase, some pupils may be interested in the more rigorous approach of deducing the equality of the base angles from the definition which refers only to equal sides. A proof of this deduction which uses congruent triangles is shown below.

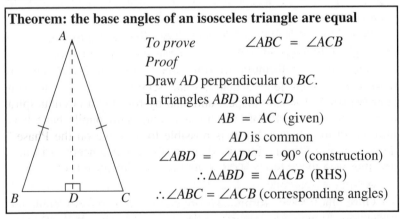

Theorem: the base angles of an isosceles triangle are equal

To prove $\angle ABC = \angle ACB$

Proof

Draw AD perpendicular to BC.

In triangles ABD and ACD

$$AB = AC \text{ (given)}$$

$$AD \text{ is common}$$

$$\angle ABD = \angle ADC = 90° \text{ (construction)}$$

$$\therefore \triangle ABD \equiv \triangle ACB \text{ (RHS)}$$

$$\therefore \angle ABC = \angle ACB \text{ (corresponding angles)}$$

Angles in triangles

Able pupils aged fourteen to sixteen will be familiar with the fact that angles in triangles are supplementary, and hopefully have been given some explanation for it. Whether or not this is the case it is useful to review a number of ways of demonstrating and proving this and discussing the relative merits of the various methods.

One such discussion, with a class of twenty-five able fifteen and sixteen year old pupils, began by showing the pupils the several demonstrations and proofs described in Chapters 2 and 3. They had met some of the explanations and proofs previously but others were new ideas.

First they were reminded of work they had done at the start of secondary school that, if the corners of a triangle are cut or torn off, they can be fitted together so that they appeared to make a straight line. The pupils seemed to appreciate that this was not tantamount to a proof. They were then shown the more precise version of this and seemed satisfied that this overcame the deficiencies of the previous version. The method of rotating a metre rule was demonstrated but was obviously perceived as being less convincing. The fourth visual proof demonstrated was that using wooden rods and relying on transformational reasoning, which was followed by the more formal equivalent. Finally the two Euclidean proofs given in Chapter 3 were constructed through a class discussion which was accompanied by diagrams and written statements on the board.

When asked which of the six "proofs" they preferred, the pupils all opted for one of the last two because they were more convincing. While a more formal approach to Euclidean geometry may be suitable for some pupils a discussion such as these pupils had seems to highlight the difference between proof and demonstration in the context of geometry, and well illustrates the power of proof.

If time and pupil interest permit it is worthwhile continuing this discussion to raise pupil awareness of some of the vocabulary and symbols used in proof. For instance, a corollary of the theorem that angles of a triangle are supplementary is that an exterior angle equals the sum of the interior opposite angles. The fact that the angles of a quadrilateral sum to $360°$ because it can be dissected into two triangles by a diagonal, is another corollary of this theorem.

A simple example of a converse is of the Isosceles Triangle Theorem that if two angles of a triangle are equal then the triangle is isosceles. A second example relates to the fact that triangles tessellate. Pupils may have been told during Proof Phase 1 that the angle sum is $180°$ because triangles tessellate . In fact there is an error in this. It is the converse which is true. Triangles tessellate because the angle sum is $180°$. Further, the converse of the original theorem is not necessarily true as three supplementary angles are not necessarily the angles of a triangle. Using the symbolic language of mathematics this can be written as:–

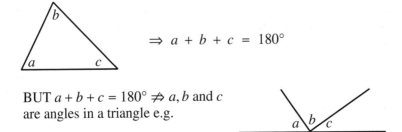

$$\Rightarrow a + b + c = 180°$$

BUT $a + b + c = 180° \nRightarrow a, b$ and c
are angles in a triangle e.g.

Two additional converses worth considering are those relating to alternate and corresponding angles between parallel lines. The following statements about these also include use of the symbols for implication and equivalence.

Theorem	Converse	Equivalence
$AB \parallel CD \Rightarrow p = q$	$p = q \Rightarrow AB \parallel CD$	$AB \parallel CD \Leftrightarrow p = q$
$AB \parallel CD \Rightarrow p = r$	$p = r \Rightarrow AB \parallel CD$	$AB \parallel CD \Leftrightarrow p = q$

Angles in circles

Properties about angles in circles are included in many secondary mathematics curricula. It is not satisfactory to present these as facts to be used to solve further problems, especially for pupils who have come to expect proofs. The work on angles in circles using investigative methods is discussed in the next section as a Proof Activity and includes a description of the difficulties the pupils in the experimental group experienced in creating a proof independently. Teachers of sixteen year old pupils, who need only a short time to form conjectures, may prefer to minimise the investigative aspect, and it is then possible to derive the proof within about one hour.

A diagrammatic form of the proof as proposed by Skemp (1971, p 99) is worth considering as an alternative to the traditional verbal-algebraic form. On several occasions when this has been used with able fifteen and sixteen year olds, and also some very able fourteen year olds, it has been well received. When the pupils have been asked which they prefer about one quarter of them express a preference for each approach and the remaining half express no preference. During the stage of constructing the proof the two

Theorem: the angle at the centre of a circle is twice any angle at the circumference (standing on the same arc).

To prove

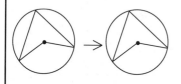

$\angle AOB = 2 \times \angle ABC$

Proof

Join *CO* and
produce to *D*.

(because)

$CO = AO$ (radii of circle)

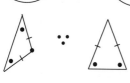

$\angle OCA = \angle OCA$
(base angles of isosceles triangle)

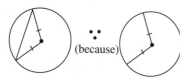

$\angle AOD = 2 \times \angle ACO$
(exterior angle of a triangle equals
the sum of interior opposite angles)

Also

Similarly
$\angle DOB = 2 \times \angle OCB$

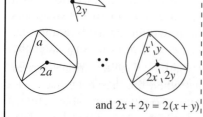

and $2x + 2y = 2(x + y)$

$\angle AOB = \angle AOD + \angle DOB$
$= 2 \times \angle ACO + 2 \times \angle DCB$
$= 2 \times (\angle ACO + \angle DCB)$
$= 2 \times \angle ACB$

approaches can be presented either simultaneously or consecutively. Diagrams on the board, or an overhead projector, or animated computer graphics can all help the class discussion. It is important to show pupils a written version or add written statements to diagrams partly so that they have some experience of "traditional" mathematics. Additionally pupils with a distinct preference for a verbal approach will not be disadvantaged due to neglect of their preferred approach. Pupils should be discouraged from copying proofs during the discussion, either promising time for this later, or by providing a printed version. Both versions are shown below. They could be issued to pupils before or after class discussion. If the proofs are to be discussed consecutively pupils should be told to fold the sheet along the dotted line. In this way the proofs can be discussed separately, and any comparisons made when both have been discussed.

The corollaries to this theorem, namely that all angles at the circumference are equal, that the angle in a semi-circle is a right-angle, and that opposite angles of a cyclic quadrilateral are supplementary are discussed in the Proof Activities section in this chapter.

Properties of tangents

1. Radius perpendicular to tangent

This first property of tangents, that a radius and tangent are mutually perpendicular at the point of contact, was introduced to the experimental group by sketching a line of symmetry in a diagram of a disc rolling along a horizontal ground. These pupils readily accepted the need to prove this conjecture and there were no obvious negative reactions to this, even when they were told to think hard as the proof started by "pretending" – a word used in conjunction with "assuming" – that the conjecture was false. The following diagrams and the salient features of the proof were written on the board during the class discussion. The pupils were given a printed copy after the discussion and the opportunity to read it through and ask any questions if there was anything they did not understand.

A proof by contradiction

Theorem: a tangent is perpendicular to the radius drawn through the point of contact.

To prove

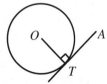

$\angle OTA = 90°$ where O is the centre of the circle and TA is a tangent to the circle at T.

Proof

TA is a tangent to the circle and OT is the radius from the point of contact T.

Assume that $\angle OTA$ is **not** 90°.

Then it is possible to draw OS so that $\angle OST = 90°$ i.e. so that OS is perpendicular to the tangent TA.

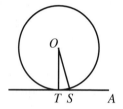

$\therefore$ Triangle OST has a right-angle at S.

Hence OT is the hypotenuse (opposite the right angle); and so $OT > OS$ (or $OS < OT$).

$\therefore$ S is inside the circle, as OT is a radius.

$\therefore$ the straight line through T and S must cut the circle again.

But this is impossible because the line through T, S, and A is a tangent.

Hence the original assumption that $\angle OTA$ is not 90° is wrong.

$\therefore$ $\angle OTA = 90°$.

i.e. the tangent TA is perpendicular to the radius OT at T.

The pupils were shown that TA was a tangent to a circle with point of contact at T and a radius was drawn from T to the centre (O) of the circle. It was then explained that if the angle formed by the radius and tangent was not a right-angle another line could be drawn from a different point (S) on the tangent to the centre of the circle that was at right-angles to the tangent. This would form a right-angled triangle of which the radius would be the hypotenuse and therefore longer than the alternative line. When the class was asked what this proved about the point S several recognised that it would be inside the circle. The others seemed to understand this and that the line TS

would then cut the circle twice, which contradicted the fact that *TS* was a tangent with only one point of contact.

The pupils seemed to have no difficulty with the idea that, as the proof had been logically argued at each step, this contradiction had arisen because of our initial assumption and that therefore it had be wrong. They accepted the fact that we had therefore proved that the original conjecture was correct and no-one asked for further clarification when invited to ask questions. It is possible that some pupils did not understand the notion of proof by contradiction in depth but most seemed to have at least a superficial appreciation of it. Some pupils who were interviewed later said that the proof had made sense to them, either at the time or when they read it through at home.

However the quality of associated written work of the pupils in the experimental group, most of whom were then at Proof Levels 3 and 4, was poor. It is therefore recommended that this topic is more appropriate during this phase catering for pupils mainly at Proof Level 5.

2. The Alternate Segment Theorem

At the beginning of a lesson on this topic the pupils in the experimental group were asked to draw a circle with a chord and tangent from a point on the circumference and measure the angle enclosed, and then draw and measure an angle in the alternate segment. They agreed that, within the limits of their ability to draw and measure accurately, these two angles seemed to be the same. They then accepted the need to prove that this was true for all such pairs of angles. When the Euclidean proof, shown below, was discussed all steps were suggested by pupils. They seemed to understand the argument. They were also able to identify the alternate segment after an exercise which practised this. The theorem was then used in a problem solved on the board.

As they worked through an exercise of similar problems only a minority of pupils seemed to gain in competence and confidence, a few showing pleasure in being able to complete problems independently. However, for the majority their responses were either incomplete or incorrect. Some pupils failed to justify statements, some made incorrect assumptions, and a few included invalid reasons. The most common error was to assume that two tangents were perpendicular because they looked perpendicular (the correct value of the angle was 86°).

The difficulties experienced by these pupils in the experimental group indicate that this work is more appropriate during Phase 3 when pupils are mainly at Proof Level 5, rather than when pupils are at Proof Levels 3 and 4. Many pupils find the formal proof difficult. However in subsequent lessons with able fifteen and sixteen year old pupils a diagrammatic equivalent has been well received by some pupils. Both versions of the proof are shown below.

The Alternate Segment Theorem:

i.e. an angle between a chord and a tangent is equal to any angle in the alternate segment.

To prove

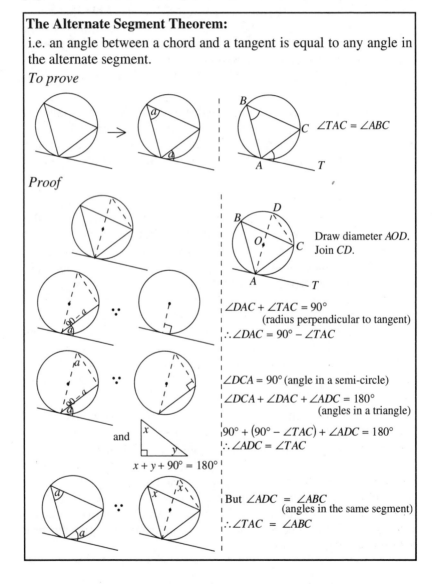

$\angle TAC = \angle ABC$

Proof

Draw diameter *AOD*.
Join *CD*.

$\angle DAC + \angle TAC = 90°$
   (radius perpendicular to tangent)
$\therefore \angle DAC = 90° - \angle TAC$

$\angle DCA = 90°$ (angle in a semi-circle)

$\angle DCA + \angle DAC + \angle ADC = 180°$
   (angles in a triangle)

$90° + (90° - \angle TAC) + \angle ADC = 180°$
$\therefore \angle ADC = \angle TAC$

$x + y + 90° = 180°$

But $\angle ADC = \angle ABC$
   (angles in the same segment)
$\therefore \angle TAC = \angle ABC$

3. Tangents from a point are equal

This property can be deduced, from knowledge that a radius and tangent are mutually perpendicular, either by reference to symmetry about the line joining the external point to the centre of the circle, or by using congruent triangles. The selection of proof and the degree of formality of style will depend on prior experience of pupils and so is left to the discretion of the teacher.

Pythagoras' Theorem

Pupils who have previously proved Pythagoras' theorem are likely only to have written an outline proof. Pupils could develop a different and complete proof through class discussion during Phase 3. As already stated in Chapter 3 there are many proofs and the two selected here are based first on equal areas and then on similar triangles.

Pythagoras' Theorem (Proof 1)

To prove: the square on the hypotenuse of a right-angled triangle is equal to the sum of the squares on the other two sides

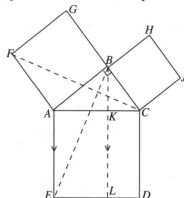

Area $ACDE$
= Area $ABGF$ + Area $BCJH$
i.e. $AC^2 = AB^2 + BC^2$

Join BE and CF.
Draw BKL parallel to AE.

Proof

$\angle CBA = 90°$ (given)

$\angle ABG = 90°$ (angle in a square)

CBG is a straight line (adjacent angles sum to 180°)

∴ Area $\triangle FAC$ = ½ area square $ABGF$
                        (same base AF, same parallels AF, GC)

Also Area $\triangle BAE$ = ½ area rectangle $AKLE$
                        (same base AE, same parallels AE, BL)

In $\triangle$s FAC, BAE $FA = AB$ (sides of square)

                        $AC = AE$ (sides of square)

                        $\angle FAC = \angle BAE$ (each $= 90° + \angle BAC$)

∴ $\triangle$s FAC, BAE are congruent (SAS)

∴ Area $\triangle FAC$ = Area $\triangle BAE$

∴ Area ½ square $ABGF$ = ½ area rectangle $AKLE$

∴ Area square $ABGF$ = area rectangle $AKLE$

Similarly   Area square $CBHJ$ = area rectangle $CKLD$

But Area rectangle $AKLE$ + area rectangle $CKLD$
                                        = area square $ACDE$

∴ Area square $ACDE$ = area square $ABGF$ + area square $CBHJ$

i.e. $AC^2 = AB^2 + BC^2$

Pythagoras' Theorem (Proof 2)

To prove: the square on the hypotenuse of a right-angled triangle is equal to the sum of the squares on the other two sides

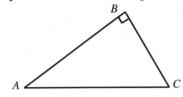

$$AC^2 = AB^2 + BC^2$$

Proof

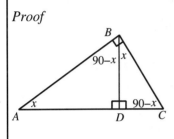

In $\triangle ABC$, $\angle ABC = 90°$
Let $\angle BAC = x°$ then $\angle BCA = (90-x)°$
Draw BD perpendicular to AC.
In $\triangle ADB$, $\angle ADB = 90°$.
$\angle BAD = x°$ and $\angle ABD = (90-x)°$
In $\triangle BDC$, $\angle BDC = 90°$.
$\angle DBC = x°$ and $\angle DCB = (90-x)°$

$\triangle s \, \dfrac{ABC}{ADB}$ are equiangular $\triangle s \, \dfrac{ABC}{BDC}$ are equiangular

$\therefore \triangle s \, \dfrac{ABC}{ADB}$ are similar $\therefore \triangle s \, \dfrac{ABC}{BDC}$ are similar

$\therefore \dfrac{AB}{AD} = \dfrac{BC}{DB} = \dfrac{AC}{AB}$ $\therefore \dfrac{AB}{BD} = \dfrac{BC}{DC} = \dfrac{AC}{BC}$

$\therefore AB^2 = AC \times AD$ (1) $\therefore BC^2 = AC \times AD$ (2)

Adding (1) and (2) gives

$$AB^2 + BC^2 = AC \times AD + AC \times CD$$
$$= AC(AD + CD)$$
$$= AC \times AC \quad (AD + DC = AC)$$
$$= AC^2$$
$$\text{i.e. } AC^2 = AB^2 + BC^2$$

Trigonometry

Although pupils at this stage may well be familiar with the use of the three trigonometric ratios, sine, cosine, and tangent, they are unlikely to have considered proofs like:–

i)   Prove that there are six possible ratios. (This is an example of proof by exhaustion.)

ii) Prove that three ratios are sufficient for calculations.

Pupils may appreciate that the reciprocal ratios (cosecant, secant, and cotangent) are superfluous, but be interested to know their names. They could also prove that $\sin a = \cos(90° - a)$ either through class discussion or using written responses to the following challenge. This was included in a written test given to pupils in the experimental and two control groups during the research.

Complementary angles

a	b	$\sin a - \cos b$
10°	80°	
20°	70°	
30°	60°	
40°		
50°		
60°		
70°		
80°		

a) In this table continue the pattern in the second column.

b) What do you notice about the values of a and b in each row.

c) Use your calculator to complete the third column and describe what you find.

d) Write down three other pairs of values for a and b for which the same result is true.

e) Use you knowledge about trigonometrical ratios in right-angled triangles to explain why this result occurs for suitable values of a and b.

This may seem too simple for able pupils but it is interesting to note that only one pupil in the experimental group explained why $\sin a = \cos(90° - a)$ even though all pupils recognised the fact that $a + b = 90°$ and were familiar with trigonometry of right-angled triangles. Clearly these able Year 10 pupils were unable to create this proof unaided. The following responses, made by a girl of low ability for the experimental group (i.e. at about the 25th percentile) during an interview, illustrate the confusion some pupils have in relating unknown variables (lengths and angles) intrinsic to the construction of such a generalised proof.

I: We need the cosine ratio for b. What is it?

     P: It's ....

I: What is adjacent to b?

     P: It's y ..... or is it? It's probably neither! (laughs)

I: You're not very sure about this are you?

     P: (laughs)

I: We're looking at angle b and we want to know what's next to it.

     P: It can't be y can it?

I: Why not?   P: Because we've had it before, haven't we?

I: But is it?   P: Yes.

I: It is that one.   P: It opens out there (points correctly).

I: Is that how you decide?

     P: Yes. But I thought we'd had that before.

     Do you know what I mean?

I: You thought you'd used it before so you couldn't use it again.

     P: Yes.

I: That's interesting. That puts you off sometimes, does it?

     P: Yes.

Sine and Cosine Rules

Most pupils at this level are required to use the Sine and Cosine Rules to solve problems about non-right-angled triangles. Although essentially trigonometry, the proofs of these relationships are heavily dependent on the use of algebra. However, for pupils working at this level this should not be a major stumbling block. Again, it would be unsatisfactory to state these results without proof to pupils familiar with the notion of proof.

Proof Activities

Although most of the investigations in this section give rise to results which are then proved using deductive methods, there is a more formal use of induction as a method of proof, and also an example of a proof by exhaustion.

Pupil Challenge

Angles in circles

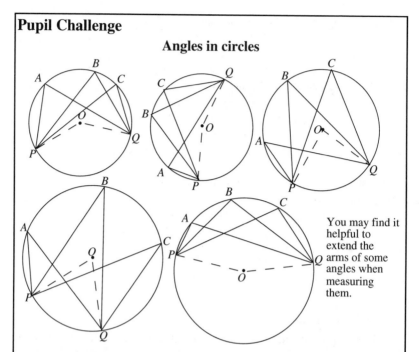

You may find it
helpful to
extend the
arms of some
angles when
measuring
them.

In each diagram above angles *A*, *B*, *C*, *D*, and *O* are standing on
(subtended by) an arc *PQ* of a circle centre *O*.

1. In each diagram measure angles *A*, *B*, and *C* and record the
   results in a table:

Diagram	*A*	*B*	*C*
1			
2			

2. What seems to be true in each case?

3. In each diagram draw another angle
   standing on arc *PQ* and label it *D*. Predict
   the size of angle *D* and then measure it.
   If your predicted and measured values
   agree record them in column *D* in the
   table. If not re-measure angle *D*.

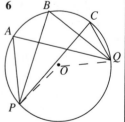

4. In diagram 6 measure angle *A* and
   predict the size of angles *B* and *C*. Check your predictions.
   On what basis did you make them?

5. In all diagrams measure the angle at the centre of the circle marked O, and record in your table, as column O.

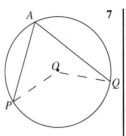

6. What seems to be true in each case?

7. In diagram 7 measure angle A and then predict the size of angle O.

   Check your prediction by measuring.

   On what basis did you make your prediction?

8. There is a connection between correct answers to questions 2 and 6. What is it?

You now have two related conjectures arising out of results of measurements in seven circles.

Lesson Outline

Angles in circles

Introduction (40 minutes)

1. Explain task.
2. Pupils measure given angles and form conjecture.
3. Explain how to draw an additional angle in each diagram.
4. Pupils continue investigation, sharing ideas.

Proof (20 minutes)

1. See "ordered questions" below to guide class discussion, to establish that angles at the circumference are twice that at the centre, standing on the same arc.

   (If desired) Consider diagrammatic proof.

2. Remind pupils that they also found angles at the circumference to be equal, and ask them to explain why.
3. Consider angle in a semi-circle.
4. Consider opposite angles in a cyclic quadrilateral (if time, or in a later lesson).

The pupils in the experimental group spent about forty minutes measuring angles and forming conjectures. They then attempted a written proof about angles in circles, under test conditions, based on the structured questions shown below. Because of their limited success in the test, the aim of subsequent lessons on this topic has been to establish conjectures through measuring, and then to create deductive proofs through class discussion. The questions shown below form the basis for this and are therefore referred to in the Lesson Outline. Despite the fact that even able pupils find creating such proofs difficult they can be led to create and understand a proof through class discussion.

To prove: the angle at the centre of a circle is equal to twice any angle at the circumference standing on the same arc.

Proof

This diagram has the same form as diagram 7 on the worksheet, with the line *AON* through the centre of the circle, added.

It divides angle *PAQ* into two parts of sizes $x°$ and $y°$.

Write down the size of angle *PAQ*.

What can you say about *OP*, *OA*, and *OQ*? .... Why?

What kinds of triangles are *OAP* and *OAQ*? .... Why?

What are the sizes of angles *OPA* and *OQA*? .... Why?

What are the sizes of angles *AOP* and *AOQ*? .... Why?

What are the sizes of angles *PON* and *QON*? .... Why?

Write down the size of angle *POQ*.

What is the connection between angle *POQ* and angle *PAQ*?

Was angle *A* special in any way?

Would the above argument apply to any angle at the circumference?

What can you deduce about such angles?

   Extension

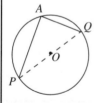

In this diagram *PQ* is the diameter of the circle.

What is the size of angle *POQ*? .... Why?

What can you deduce about angle *APQ*? .... Why?

Write down a general conclusion.

Lesson – Introduction

   Pupils should measure angles in diagrams provided on the pupil worksheet, or copied from the board, in order to observe the apparent fact that angles at the circumference of a circle subtended by the same arc are equal to each other, and to half a corresponding angle at the centre. Initially pupils should only attempt Tasks 1 and 2 in the worksheet. When appropriate explain how to add an angle of their own, label it D, and then predict, measure and record its value. Most pupils will then be able to continue without further teacher assistance. During this part of the lesson pupils could compare measurements and share ideas about observations and to attempt explanations. They may need to be reminded that conclusions based on measuring particular diagrams do not constitute a proof.

Pupil responses

After initial class discussion about the first question, to establish that any angle at the circumference was $(x + y)$, the pupils in the experimental group were asked to answer the remaining questions under test conditions, and their written answers scrutinised by the author.

Although the pupils seemed to be on task for about fifteen minutes their success was very limited and in this test no pupil produced a complete, correct proof. About one third of the pupils correctly wrote that angle $POQ = 2(x + y)$ but gave as the reason that which they were attempting to prove. These pupils appeared to be at Proof Level 3 in that they demonstrated an awareness of what constitutes a generalised proof, but were still prone to using circular arguments. Also at Proof Level 3 were those who were confused over whether angle A was special, and whether or not the proof applied to any angle. Only five pupils gave the correct combination of responses, that angle A was not special and the proof therefore applied to any angle. Four thought that angle A was special and also that the proof was valid for any angle, but later discussion revealed misunderstanding of use of the word "special". One girl said that she had thought angle A was special because she knew that it was half the angle at the centre. Further discussion indicated that a stumbling block had been failure to recognise that AON was a straight line, and thence to deduce the sizes of the parts of the angle at the centre of the circle.

These responses indicate that these pupils are unable to create multi-step proofs like this, even with the guidance of structured questions. Not surprisingly there were more correct attempts to prove that the angle in a semi-circle is a right-angle, but not all pupils were able to do this unaided. Subsequent lessons, with pupils of similar age and ability, in which the above proof was developed through class discussion, suggest that while such pupils can understand each step in the proof, only a few of the more able understand the whole proof and are satisfied by it. Thus it is considered advisable to introduce this proof only to older and/or more able pupils, working at or towards Proof Level 5. It is therefore more appropriate for this third Proof Phase than for Proof Phase 2. Two proofs of the theorem are included in the Proof Discussions section of this chapter.

A corollary to this theorem, that opposite angles of a cyclic quadrilateral are supplementary, was presented as an investigate-prove item in the research test (Chapter 1), and is shown below.

Pupil Challenge

Opposite angles in a cyclic quadrilateral

A cyclic quadrilateral is a quadrilateral with its vertices on the circumference of a circle.

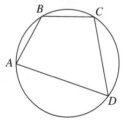
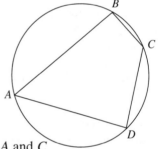

In each quadrilateral measure angles A and C carefully and write the size in each angle.

Repeat for angles B and D.

Describe what you notice about each pair of angles.

Use the diagram on the right and appropriate angle facts to explain why the result will always occur for opposite angles of any cyclic quadrilateral.

(A, B, C, and D are on the circumference of a circle centre O.)

Pupil responses

In the test nearly two thirds of each group noticed angle sums of 180° and a few identified equal angle sums. However, the only two proofs were from able pupils in the experimental group. One used an informal style and in the other the pupil had omitted reasons for the facts he used. One boy wrote, "In diagram 3 (on the question paper) the angles $x + y = 360°$; because $\frac{1}{2}x = a$ and $\frac{1}{2}y = c$, therefore $a + c = \frac{1}{2}x + y$ which $= 180°$" and the girl wrote, "The angle in the centre of a circle is O. Angles of lines coming away from this will be half of it. Therefore a will be half of x and c will be half of y. $x + y = $ "O" $= 360°$. If they (a and c) are half of two numbers whose sum is 360° they must join together to equal 180°." This last response was discussed with the girl during an interview and she was surprised that what she had written still made sense to her and even more surprised that it was essentially correct. Her comments in the interview were "I didn't think I got that right. I could remember bits of it and I had to try to piece it together to suit me." She had clearly reached the stage of being able to construct her own proof from related mathematical facts, but still was unsure about what she produced.

One boy interviewed, who had not observed that opposite angles of a cyclic quadrilateral are supplementary, was asked how he might compare his pairs of values and suggested finding differences saying, "I always find differences first, and then sums." He quickly recognised the pattern and was led to an understanding of the result. He commented, "I should have looked at it more carefully." The remaining pupils interviewed were readily led through a proof based on the diagram given in the test, even though they had been unable to do this unaided. This suggests that if the proof is developed with the pupils through discussion it is not beyond their understanding.

Pupil Challenge

Growing patterns

1.

Start with a single equilateral triangle drawn on isometric graph paper. At each stage add new equilateral triangles all round the outside. Copy and continue the following table:–

Stage number (n)	Number of 'unit' triangles (T)
1	1
2	4
3	

Describe any patterns.

Find a formula for T in terms of n.

Show how you derived your formula and explain why it will always work.

2.

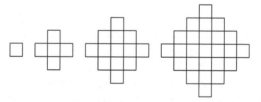

Start with a single square drawn on squared paper.

At each stage add new squares all round the outside.

Copy and continue the following table:–

Stage number (n)	Number of 'unit' squares (S)
1	1
2	5
3	

Describe any patterns.

Find a formula for S in terms of n.

Show how you derived your formula and explain why it will always work.

This investigation (Gardiner, 1987, p 88) involves spatial reasoning in building up the patterns, and in conjunction with algebra, in analysing them. Three proofs of this formula are excellent examples of "proof without words" (Nelsen, 1995) and are shown on pages 192, 193 and 194. Such proofs with diagrams are also advocated by Pope (1996). The fact that an algebraic deductive proof is also available means that this pattern is an example which can be analysed in several ways.

Lesson Outlines
Growing patterns
Lesson 1 – Growing triangles (30 – 40 minutes)
1. Pupils count triangles.
2. Record results on board.
3. Discuss results: successive differences, multiples of three, triangles, triangle numbers.

Pupil homework (40 minutes.)

Lesson 2 – Growing squares (20 – 30 minutes)
Prepare diagrams in advance.
Identify pupils whose reports include useful starting points.
1. Write one formula on board.
2. Ask named pupil to explain her/his thinking.
3. Ask follow-up questions of whole class.
4. Repeat (1), (2) and (3) for alternative approaches.
5. Reconcile differing approaches through class discussion.

Lesson 1 – Introduction
Some pupils in the experimental group were expected to find the algebraic analysis difficult. By first solving the triangle pattern in class they would be more able to solve the square pattern for homework. The square pattern is easier because each new stage is generally, but not mathematically, similar to the previous stage. In the triangle pattern alternate stages add triangles the other way up and the similarity of successive stages is not apparent unless the resulting shape is rotated through 60°. This increases the level of difficulty for some pupils.

At the beginning of a lesson the pupils were given a worksheet and set the task of counting the number of triangles at each stage as the pattern developed. Their results for the first five stages of the pattern of triangles were recorded on the board. The class discussion about proof began by considering successive differences. Pupils noticed that at each stage the number of triangles added was a multiple of three. Several pupils realised that this was because the triangle had three sides and also that the exception to adding a multiple of three was at Stage 1. So one was subtracted from the total number of triangles (T−1) and the result divided by three for each of the first five stages to see how many triangles had been added on to each side. Although most pupils seemed to follow this argument no-one recognised the resulting triangle numbers. During the remainder of the lesson it was established (not for the first time with these pupils) that these were obtained by adding consecutive integers.

Pupil reports

Pupils then analysed the "Growing Squares" pattern for homework. In the written reports all pupils continued the pattern correctly. About half of the reports used the same approach as had been discussed in the lesson for the triangular pattern. One pupil produced an exemplary report with the formula $s = 4$ (triangle number stage − 1 stage) + 1 accompanied by a diagram indicating exactly the position of the triangle numbers, which had not been discussed in the previous lesson. He demonstrates Fischbein's "insightful understanding" (1982) of this pattern.

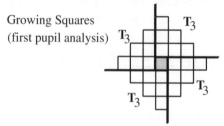

Growing Squares
(first pupil analysis)

His report concluded with the general statement that the formula could be used in any growing pattern of regular shapes as the expanding pattern would be the same and the number of unit shapes would be

Number of sides of unit × (Triangle number stage − 1stage) + 1.

While this is not mathematically rigorous it demonstrates clearly that this pupil has an excellent understanding of both pattern and proof in this instance.

Eight pupils produced the formula $s = n^2 + (n - 1)^2$ but were unable to explain it fully. Three confused checking and proof and three gave incorrect or confused explanations. Only two boys seemed to have some idea as to why this formula was appropriate and explained that a diamond was a square on its side. However neither produced a diagram to illustrate this, nor further explanation, and one confused checking and proof.

Although this was a difficult pattern for many pupils to explain it provided an opportunity for the more able pupils to exercise their talents and produce ideas which could usefully be discussed by the whole class during the next lesson.

Lesson 2 – Follow-up discussion

Diagrams clearly showing the presence of triangle numbers (see previous diagram) and the sums of squares by looking sideways at the patterns (see below) were prepared in advance. The first was shown to the class. The boy who derived the formula $s = 4 \times T_{n-1} + 1$ helped explain it to the class.

The formula $s = n^2 + (n - 1)^2$ was then written on the board and pupils invited to suggest why this should work. No-one was able to explain how this related to either the number patterns obtained or to the diagram. Eventually it was established that in most cases this result had been copied from another pupil. The two boys who had partially explained this had passed it on to their classmates but were unable to explain their thinking further when asked. This would seem to be an example of the type of thinking described by Fischbein (1982) as "intuitive" and imposed by the structure of the pattern. The class was then shown the original diagram turned sideways as in a), and asked if they could explain further. Only one boy was able to explain that because the squares were arranged in diagonal rows there were gaps between them. A few pupils were able to understand his explanation but most did not. However all pupils could understand, when they were shown the second diagram b) with the alternate diagonal rows of squares shaded differently to highlight the presence of two square sets of unit squares.

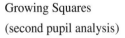 Growing Squares

(second pupil analysis)

a)   b)

A comparison of the two different approaches was discussed and some pupils took an active part in establishing the algebraic equivalence of the two formulae $s = 4 \times T_{n-1} + 1$ and $s = n^2 + (n - 1)^2$.

Although this activity was suitable for fourteen and fifteen year old pupils towards the end of a teaching programme emphasising proof it is recommended as being more appropriate for pupils who are at Proof Levels 4 or 5. On a more recent occasion a pupil at Proof Level 5 included the following dissection in his report to justify $s = n^2 + (n - 1)^2$.

Growing Squares

(third pupil analysis)

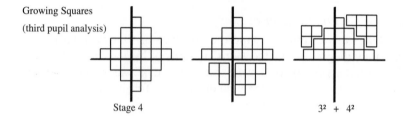

Stage 4 $3^2 + 4^2$

Pupil Challenge

Investigating polyhedra

A polyhedron (pl. polyhedra) is a solid with plane faces.

You will probably recognise these polyhedra.

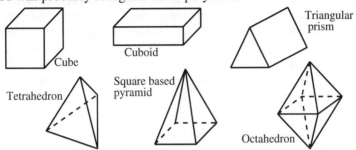

For each of these, and any others that you are given or can visualise, count the number of faces (*F*), vertices (*V*) and edges (*E*).

Record your results for prisms, pyramids, and other solids, in a table.

	Polyhedron	*F*	*V*	*E*
Prisms	Cube Cuboid Triangular			
Pyramids	Tetrahedron Square based			
Other	Octahedron Dodecahedron Icosahedron Parallelapiped			

Try to find a relationship between F, V, and E.

Try to explain it for prisms and pyramids.

Does your explanation apply to irregular solids?

Try to explain the relationship for all solids.

Lakatos (1976) uses an investigation of Euler's theorem to show that exploration is an important aspect of proof. An attractive, albeit superficial, feature of this activity is that pupils enjoy drawing, handling and naming a variety of solids. Additionally the activity provides valuable experience in a previously unfamiliar area of mathematics and also in a different style of reasoning. The proof provides an unusual example of how changing a problem facilitates its solution. Other advantages are that the relation is not obvious, that in obtaining results pupils gain valuable practice in thinking in three dimensions, and in searching for a relation between the variables they are exercising pattern-spotting skills.

This activity was undertaken with the pupils in the experimental group towards the end of the teaching programme. They were allowed about twenty minutes to collect results from pictures on posters and handling plastic and wooden solids. They enjoyed this and also meeting words like parallelapiped, trapezoidal prism, and icosahedron. However a few pupils were unsure about mathematical terms such as plane and vertex and so these were defined for the class. One girl argued that flat and corner were better because she understood them but accepted the point that she would not become familiar with mathematical terms if they were never used. The activity has since been used with able fifteen and sixteen year old pupils and, on a separate occasion, with very able (above the tenth percentile) pupils of the same age. This latter group was instructed to investigate polyhedra and networks simultaneously and search for possible connections.

While both groups of able pupils could obtain results, find the relationship, and understand the proofs when they were discussed, some pupils in the latter group of very able pupils could produce their own proofs of the results for prisms and pyramids, with little or no teacher intervention. In the discussions with the former two groups pupils realised the need for a proof, especially when there were some errors of counting. Most pupils were interested and many were actively involved in the discussion inasmuch as they responded to teacher led questioning. The proofs created by the very able pupils provide a useful framework for class discussion of prisms and pyramids and are included in the proof provided below.

Euler's Theorem

To prove

$$F + V - E = 2 \qquad \text{and} \qquad R + N - A = 2$$

for plane solids with   for networks with

F faces, V vertices, E edges R regions, N nodes, A arcs

Proofs

1. A prism whose cross-section is a polygon with n sides has:–

   $n + 2$ faces (a set of n faces along the length and one face at each end)

   $2n$ vertices (a set of n at each end)

   $3n$ edges (a set of n at each end and a third set of n along the length)

   Thus $F + V - E = (n + 2) + 2n - 3n = 2$

2. A pyramid whose base is a polygon with n sides has:–

   $n + 1$ faces (a set of n sloping faces and one face at the base)

   $n + 1$ vertices (a set of n vertices at the base and one vertex at the top)

   $2n$ edges (a set of n sloping edges and a set of n edges at the base)

   Thus $F + V - E = (n + 1) + (n + 1) - 2n = 2$

Other solids

The approach for prisms and pyramids is not applicable to all plane solids. An alternative proof is based on a similar property for networks which is proved by induction.

3.   The simplest network is $R = 1 \ N = 1 \ A = 1$

   $R + N - A = 1 + 2 - 1 = 2$

   It can be 'enlarged' by:–

   a) Adding only a node   so that N increases by 1 and

    A increases by 1 and thus

                                        $N - A$ remains unchanged.

   b) Adding only an arc

                                        so that A increases by 1 and

   or R increases by 1 and thus

                                        $R - A$ remains unchanged.

   c) Adding a node and an arc   so that N increases by 1 and

   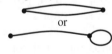   and A increases by 1 and thus

                                        $N - A$ remains unchanged.

   None of these changes affects the value of $R + N - A$.

   Thus the value is always 2, i.e. $R + N - A = 2$.

4. All plane solids are topologically equivalent to a network.

i.e.   they can be visualised as being 'squashed flat' so that faces become regions, vertices become nodes, and edges become arcs.

Thus the relationship for networks proved above is also true for all plane solids with R replaced by F, N replaced by V, and A replaced by E. i.e. $F + V - E = 2$.

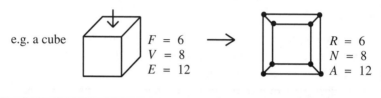

e.g. a cube $F = 6$ $R = 6$
                   $V = 8$ $N = 8$
                   $E = 12$ $A = 12$

Pupils in all three groups realised that there were some solids which were neither prisms nor pyramids, and that therefore a different approach would be required. However no pupil was able to volunteer an explanation, even among those in the third group of very able pupils who had simultaneously collected results for networks and solids and discovered Euler's relation for both. At this point it was necessary to explain the structure of networks to the pupils in the first two groups so that they could investigate these and discover Euler's relation for regions, nodes, and arcs.

The method of proof used for all solids requires pupils to transform a solid into a network by considering it to be squashed so that faces (F), vertices (V) and edges (E) became regions (R), nodes (N) and arcs (A). The inductive proof establishes that $R + N - A$ is equal to two for the simplest case, and remains constant if an arc or node is added, and thence that $R + N - A$ must always be equal to two. The topological equivalence of networks and plane solids then completes the proof of Euler's theorem for all plane solids.

The pupils in the experimental group were given the printed summary of the class discussion but the older pupils were instructed to write their own reports. Their completed reports indicated that they understood the structure of both solids and networks and the connection between them.

Pupil Challenge

Rows of squares

Rows of squares are made from 'matches'.

A: For a single row of squares find and explain formulae for:–
- a) the number of matches (m)
- b) the number of dots (d)

in terms of the number of squares (n).

B: Repeat A for a double row of squares.
C: Investigate for more rows of squares and try to generalise for r rows of n squares.

This is an extension of the simpler challenge "Row of squares" described in Chapter 2. "Rows of squares" has been used with very able pupils who had not previously met the simplest case. There was a discussion about a single row of squares as an introduction to the problem at the beginning of the lesson. Pupils were then advised to examine the case of a double row of squares and the results for this were generalised in a class discussion. The pupils were then set the task of examining the structure of rectangular grids with m by n squares to find and explain connections between the size of the grid and the numbers of matches and dots. The excerpt below is the last part of a report written by a very able boy.

To derive general formulas for 'm' and 'd', diagrams were drawn and tables constructed. To find 'm' the differences were found. When these were analysed they appeared to be '2r+1'. When $(2r+1)n$ was calculated the figures were always 1 less than 'm'. Therefore the formula for 'm' was calculated to be $m = (2r+1)n + r$. This was then checked to see if it was correct

To prove it was correct the construction of the shapes were analysed. It was seen each new square added required 2 matches, except for the first square of each new column which, required 3 and hence $(2r+1)n$:

$$r = 3 \qquad \begin{array}{l} \rule{1em}{0pt} 2+1 \\ \rule{1em}{0pt} 2 \\ \rule{1em}{0pt} 2 \end{array} \quad \begin{array}{l} \\ = (3 \times 2) + 1 \\ = 2r + 1 \end{array}$$

However, to complete the shape, each square at the end needs an extra match to be complete, because there are 'r' squares on the end, an extra 'r' amount of matches are required.

$$r = 3$$

The formula therefore has to be $m = (2r+1)n + r$.

Pupil Challenge

Special arrangements

1. Write the numbers 1, 2, 3 and 4 in a row so that the sum of any two adjacent numbers in the row is at least five.
   Find all possible solutions.
2. Write the numbers 1, 2, 3, 4 and 5 in a row so that the sum of any two adjacent numbers is at least six.
   Find all possible solutions.

This activity involves arranging digits to satisfy given conditions. It is the first part of a series of problems suggested by Anderson and Austin (1995) for use in schools and colleges to help pupils and students to "understand how proofs are constructed and that different kinds of proofs are needed in different circumstances".

When introducing the first problem it is advisable to re-iterate the need to persuade others that all solutions have been found. The pupils' initial reaction to this problem will most likely be to suggest listing all possible arrangements and then identifying those which satisfy the given condition. Although not the most efficient method this should be encouraged at this stage as it provides another example of a proof by exhaustion, and also practice in a systematic approach to problem-solving. Of the twenty-four possible arrangements of the numbers the following four conform to the given condition:–

$$1\ 4\ 2\ 3, \quad 1\ 4\ 3\ 2, \quad 2\ 3\ 4\ 1, \quad 3\ 2\ 4\ 1.$$

Another advantage of listing all arrangements is that it is possible to use the configuration "2 1 3 4" to illustrate the fact that it is only necessary to know that 2+1 is less than 5 in order to reject it. The fact that 3+1 is also less than 5 need not be considered is an illustration that one counter-example is sufficient to disprove an assertion.

Although pupils may be entirely satisfied by this approach a second, more reasoned, approach leading to a more "efficient" solution should be discussed. Consideration of the position of 1 leads to the realisation that it can only be next to 4 and must therefore be at one end. Therefore acceptable arrangements must be of the form 1 4 x y or x y 4 1, where x and y can be replaced by 2 or 3, leading to the four solutions above.

In the second problem the first approach leads to listing 120 possible arrangements and is therefore rejected in favour of the more reasoned approach. This begins in a similar way to the first problem, to justify starting with 1 5 or ending with 5 1. Additionally, since 2 and 3 cannot be adjacent and must therefore be separated by 4, possible arrangements are of the form 1 5 x 4 y and x 4 y 5 1, where x and y again are replaced by 2 and 3. Thus the only four satisfactory arrangements are:–

$$1\ 5\ 2\ 4\ 3, \quad 1\ 5\ 3\ 4\ 2, \quad 3\ 4\ 2\ 5\ 1, \quad 2\ 4\ 3\ 5\ 1.$$

When reflecting on the solutions to both problems it is worth observing how using the symmetry of the arrangements simplified the arguments.

Some teachers may wish to continue by asking pupils to consider arranging the first six (and/or seven) integers so that adjacent pairs sum to at least seven (or eight), as suggested by Anderson and Austin; but their further extensions of analysing the number of solutions is considered to be beyond all but the exceptionally able pupils. These are therefore deferred to Chapter 5 which includes suggestions for proof activities appropriate for sixth formers. There are eight arrangements for both six and seven integers and four of each are:–

> 1 6 3 4 5 2,   1 6 4 3 5 2,   1 6 2 5 3 4,   1 6 2 5 4 3;
> 1 7 2 6 4 5 3,   1 7 2 6 3 5 4,   1 7 3 5 4 6 2,   1 7 4 5 3 6 2.

The remaining arrangements are obtained by reversing these sequences.

The following three tasks formed the basis of interviews with pupils in both experimental and control groups when they were fifteen or sixteen years old. They are included here as the basis for pupil investigation followed by class discussions and written reports. The possible solutions and rationale for each task will provide guidance for leading a class discussion. The pupil responses, regarding the proof methods they used and the levels of awareness of proof they showed, will indicate the level of performance of these able pupils. The most able pupils could investigate and write reports independently, before the class discussion which will summarise their achievement and resolve any difficulties.

Interviews with pupils: Task 1 – Squares of squares

Pupil Challenge

Squares of squares

'Squares of squares' are made with matches as shown in the diagram below:

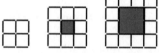

For example a 2 × 2 'square of squares' has 4 edge squares and uses 12 matches; and a 3 × 3 'square of squares' has 8 edge squares and uses 24 matches.

How many edge squares and how many matches will be needed to make a 25 × 25 'square of squares'?

There are two different approaches to this task but various combinations of these are also possible. Pupils could examine either the structure of the diagrams in order to find connections, or the numerical values in order to find number patterns. For either approach it seemed likely that pupils would count squares and matches and that their methods of doing this would influence the patterns and connections they observed.

For instance edge squares could be counted as a top set, bottom set and two side sets; or as four sets along each side around the edge; or just counted round. The first method would probably lead to two sets of n ($2n$ or $n + n$) with two sets of $n - 2$ ($2(n - 2)$ or $n - 2 + n - 2$) and thence to $4n - 4$. The second approach would lead to four sets of $n - 1$ and thence to $4(n - 1)$. Counting round could lead to recognition of either successive differences or multiples of four, and the number of fours as $n - 1$. Comparison with the structure of the diagrams explains that multiples of four arise because the grid has four sides; and that, as corner squares are in two edges, each edge has $n - 1$ independent squares, The edge squares might also be seen as those that are left when the squares in the middle are removed and the number for a 25×25 grid found by calculating the difference between 25^2 and 23^2. This could be generalised as $n^2 - (n - 2)^2$ by pupils who were fluent in their use of algebra.

The total number of matches could be the aggregate of three distinct sets – outer plus inner edge, plus partitions – or as three additional matches for each additional square around the edges in turn. Both of these could lead to recognition of a factor of three but this could also be observed by examination of numerical results. Alternatively, reliance on number patterns only might reveal successive differences, or multiples, of twelve, since the number of matches is three times the number of edge squares, which is a multiple of four.

One purpose of using Task 1 was to discover whether pupils relied on numerical values, or a diagram, or both. They could formulate a rule or describe a pattern based on observation of numerical values obtained from the particular examples given, or analyse the structure of the diagrams and extrapolate to larger squares, or use a mixture of these. Numerical values were quoted in order to provide pupils with a confident start although this might have introduced a possible bias to the numerical approach. Verbal clarification to pupils that the space in the middle of the diagrams was shaded to indicate that these squares were not under consideration would aid understanding of the task, and also counter-balance the possible numerical bias with a reference to the structure of the diagrams.

Discussion of this problem of a type familiar to the pupils in the experimental group would show any differences between these pupils' responses and those in the two control groups. The task was appropriate for pupils in all three groups in that they could find the numerical answers required, but some pupils experienced difficulty in explaining the results.

No pupil relied wholly on diagrams but six considered diagrams and numbers, although in each case inspection of diagrams was to check ideas arising from inspection of numbers. None started by analysing the structure of the diagram in order to find a formula. One boy initially asked if he could draw more diagrams but then, having re-examined his table of values, said he would not need to as he could see some patterns. Another boy had problems counting accurately and found this frustrating obviously much preferring to look for number patterns.

After recognising that the number of edge squares was a multiple of four, all but two boys in control groups explained eventually that this was because a square has four sides. Except for one of these they all explained that the other factor was $(n - 1)$ because corner squares had been counted twice. The exception said that four was subtracted from $4n$ for the same reason. One girl in a control group recognised multiples of four but explained the pattern as "$2 \times n$ (top and bottom) $+ 2 \times (n - 2)$ (to remove the corners from the sides)". A girl in the experimental group, who also noticed multiples of four during the pattern-spotting process, attempted to explain why the numbers of squares in the shaded section were 1, 4, 9, and 16. She did not recognise they were square numbers and could not explain why the successive differences were 3, 5, and 7. She struggled with this for some time before noticing again the presence of multiples of four which she was able to explain. All twelve pupils who recognised that $m = 3e$ could eventually explain that each new square added three new matches. Five pupils observed multiples or differences of twelve and could not explain these, but further questioning led to recognition and understanding of $m = 3e$. One girl in the experimental group was able to explain why there were multiples of twelve.

Interviews with pupils: Task 2 – One less than square

> ## Pupil Challenge
> ### One less than square
> Look at this pattern:
>
> Line 1 $2^2 - 1 = 3 = 1 \times 3$
>
> Line 2 $3^2 - 1 = 8 = 2 \times 4$
>
> Line 3 $4^2 - 1 = 15 = 3 \times 5$
>
> Find, without using a calculator, the value of $999^2 - 1$.

There are several number patterns that pupils could observe. They could see sets of consecutive integers, the numbers in the product on the right hand side of the identity are one less and one more than the line number squared, or a difference of two between these and the first is the same as the line number which is one less than the number squared. It is possible that some pupils may see that successive differences between the middle numbers in each identity are consecutive odd numbers.

In explaining why these patterns occur pupils could use an algebraic approach, representing the number squared by n and the right hand product as $(n - 1) \times (n + 1)$ and realising that this is equivalent to $n^2 - 1$. Alternatively they could draw a suitable diagram showing how the shape left when a unit square is removed from the corner of a larger square can be dissected and reformed to make a rectangle $(n - 1)$ by $(n + 1)$ as shown below.

A Proof without words for Task 2

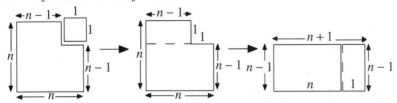

This task was included as an example of a pattern that could be analysed algebraically or diagrammatically. Most pupils could recognise at least one pattern in this task but not all recognised all patterns necessary to answer the question or be able to explain the structure of the pattern.

The experience of the written Proof Test and of an earlier set of interviews suggested that pupils would find this task more difficult than Task 1. Care was exercised in questioning to avoid directing pupils to a particular method of solution, until it was clear that further progress was unlikely without direct questions. After an algebraic solution, the possibility of an alternative approach was raised. A diagrammatic proof was discussed, to find out whether or not a "proof without words" was perceived as being easier to understand, as suggested by Pope (1996).

All pupils eventually explained why $n^2 - 1 = (n - 1)(n + 1)$, using algebra, with varying degrees of help. None spontaneously suggested drawing a diagram and, even when asked at least twice if they could think of an alternative representation to algebra, all but one had no further suggestions. This boy was initially unsure what was meant by explanation without using algebra but half way through a repeat of the question he said that he could draw it. However, he was unsure how to proceed and even talked of removing matches! As he had understood the algebraic argument, it was considered unwise to develop the diagrammatic approach in order to allow sufficient time for the third task. This same conclusion was also reached in the majority of the interviews. An able boy in the experimental group, and a weaker girl in a control group, when asked whether a diagram would help, responded that they were quite satisfied with the algebraic explanation. Again it was considered unwise to pursue a diagrammatic proof and therefore it was not possible to discover whether these pupils found such proofs easier to understand.

Interviews with pupils: Task 3 – Reverse and subtract

Pupil Challenge

Reverse and subtract

In the following subtractions the second number has been formed by reversing the digits of the first:

$\qquad$ 73 − 73 = $\qquad$ 52 − 25 = $\qquad$ 60 − 06 =

Find the answers to these subtractions.

Use connections between the results to find 94 − 49 without subtraction!

Although the solution to this task depends on recognising multiples of nine some pupils might recognise multiples of three instead, or in addition. A second embedded number pattern is that the number of nines is the same as the difference between the digits. A possible algebraic proof represents the first number as $10a + b$ and the second as $10b + a$. The difference can then be expressed as $(10a + b) - (10b + a) = 9(a - b)$. However a more likely explanation, for pupils, is based on the analysis of a particular subtraction as a crucial experiment or generic example, e.g. $73 - 37 = (7 - 3) \times 10 + (3 - 7) = 10 \times (7 - 3) - (7 - 3) = 9 \times (7 - 3)$.

The purpose of this task was to investigate how pupils attempt to analyse embedded patterns (e.g. multiples of nine) when they are not part of a growing structure. Responses to questions of this type in the Proof Test, in the end-of-year examination, and in the first set of interviews, suggest pupils find these patterns difficult to analyse. The task is similar to that used in a UK mathematics competition whose results caused Gardiner (1995b) to suggest that the teaching received by only a few pupils had allowed them to appreciate the solution.

Personal experience in the classroom suggests that a few able pupils aged eleven and twelve years can appreciate an informal explanation, such as the inductive proof above, of this task and students of A-level Mathematics can construct an algebraic proof. Thus the level of difficulty (to include explanation) was thought to be appropriate for the fifteen and sixteen year old pupils in this research. It has the advantage that other examples are easily obtainable and so pupils would be able to take an active part in the interview rather than simply respond to closed questions if, as seemed likely, they were unable to make progress.

There was only one tentative attempt to use algebra. A girl in the experimental group, considering the proof for this, wrote n to represent a number but realised she could not do so with "just n". She contemplated using $n1$ and $n2$ but did not think that would work either. The interviewer suggested she might prefer a and b and she wrote $ab - ba = (a - b) \times 9$. However she was unable to explain how ab represented a number and wondered how to represent 94 in algebraic form. She returned to her "equation" and expanded $(a - b) \times 9$ as $9a - 9b$ but could go no further. She did, however, realise that $ab - ba = 0$ and that therefore something was wrong but she was unable to explain what it was. It was decided that use of $10a + b$ might confuse the girl and an explanation was discussed in terms of $94 - 49$ followed by an apparent appreciation that this could be generalised. This inductive approach was adopted with all other interviewees. The negligible success rate of pupils formally explaining this pattern reflects the low success rate of able, slightly younger, pupils in explaining a related pattern in the mathematics competition, referred to above.

Pupil awareness of proof in interview tasks

The reactions of all pupils in the experimental group indicated that they began at Proof Level 2 or above. In contrast, about half of the pupils in the control groups were either bemused by the request for an explanation or suggested considering special cases, e.g. drawing the 5×5 grid to check, indicating they were at Proof Level 0 or 1. Two thirds of the pupils increased their proof levels during interview. For instance, seven pupils in the control groups had no intuitive appreciation that an explanation existed, but during discussion were led to an understanding of the structure of a pattern, suggesting possible progress from Proof Level 0 to 3.

In Task 2 one girl in a control group, when asked if the connection she described was always true, suggested that she could test for $n = 20$. However when the question was repeated said that she thought it was true but that she did not know how to prove it. She said "I can't test loads!" She had attained Proof Level 2a. When asked if she could apply the idea to any number in general she suggested using an "equation with n". She was able to write down a correct algebraic statement but needed some help in establishing its universal validity, at which point she seemed able to appreciate that she had constructed a proof, and had thus appeared to have progressed to Proof Level 3.

One boy in a control group was taken aback by the idea that there might be an explanation of the patterns and the only suggestion he could offer in Task 1 was a reference to odd and even numbers. He then conceded that there probably was a reason but he could not find it. In Task 3 he was not surprised by the request for an explanation but could only suggest that it might be "some weird phenomenon!" However although the idea of explaining mathematical connections seemed novel to him he was clearly interested and voluntarily said that he had learned something from the interview. He seemed to have progressed from Proof Level 0 to 3.

A boy in the experimental group, wrote an algebraic statement of the pattern in Task 2, and suggested he could prove it using random numbers (Proof Level 2a). When he was asked if he was sure this was sufficient he realised the need for something more general (Proof Level 3). This was a similar response to four other pupils including the girl described above who initially confused proof and substitution but soon realised the error in this. A boy in a control group suggested substitution as a means of making sure that the pattern was always true but was very hesitant to admit that he was convinced by this. He then realised the need for a general approach. A second boy in a control group gave three examples and then realised the tediousness of continuing with other examples. These four pupils also demonstrate possible progression to Proof Level 3.

The fact that fewer than half of the pupils in the control groups could explain patterns without reference to particular cases is in line with the findings of Fischbein and Kedem (1982). They showed that only a minority of pupils, across the whole ability range, could distinguish between empirical and formal proof. In the experimental group nearly three quarters could explain patterns without using particular cases (Proof Level 3 or above), providing further evidence to support Bell's (1983) claim that this may be sensitive to direct teaching. In all cases it was possible to either create a proof with a pupil, or describe a proof in terms they could understand. All seemed satisfied finally that for Tasks 1 and 2 they had constructed an argument which showed each statement was universally true, and thus had attained Proof Level 3 or above. Although a generalised proof was not constructed in Task 3 all pupils understood the use of a a particular case as a generic example. and thus appeared to have attained Proof level 2b.

"Not Proof"

One purpose of this section is to show, in greater depth than previously, the difference between a generalised proof and an inference based on examination of empirical evidence from a limited number of particular cases, or a demonstration of truth for a special case. The paradoxes considered here highlight the need for precision in proof by recognising the difference between zero and infinitesimally small, and appreciating the error induced by treating a continuous variable as being discrete.

Volume of a pyramid

Empirical evidence

In preparation for a lesson on the volume of a pyramid pupils had been given the task of making two pyramids from card and estimating the volume by filling with water. During the lesson pupils' measurements of pyramids were collated in two tables on the board. One listed dimensions of square based pyramids, under headings length (l), breadth (b), and height (h); the other listed dimensions of cones under headings diameter (d), radius (r), and height (h); and both included a column recording measured volume (V). The likelihood that volume, which is measured in cubic units, should be related to the product of three dimensions was discussed and the link with areas of ends of prisms led to the calculation and recording of the value of the area of base multiplied by height ($A \times h$). It had been anticipated that, as on a previous occasion, suitable approximations of the measured volumes would highlight the existence of the factor of three ($A \times h = 3V$), but it was apparent from the pupils' measurements that this was highly unlikely on this occasion. An alternative approach was needed.

Class discussion eventually led to the suggestion that a graph may be a useful way of illustrating the data. Whether the graph would be curved or straight, and whether it passed through the origin were considered and, despite the inaccuracies of measuring, all the relevant points were plotted as the pupils were familiar with the idea of line of best fit. The values of the gradient were mostly in the range 0.25 and 0.4. The value of 0.3 was readily accepted as a class average and compared favourably with the value suggested by the formula for the volume of a pyramid, which was brought to the attention of the pupils at this point. It was again emphasised that although the graph provided strong evidence for the truth of the formula it was not tantamount to proof. A general proof for all pyramids was not accessible to these pupils but a demonstration model of a cube dissected into six square-based pyramids provided a proof for such pyramids.

Demonstration

It can be shown that six square based (of side l) pyramids whose height is ½l, can be arranged, with vertices meeting, to form a cube. Thus the volume of each pyramid is therefore one sixth the volume of the cube ($\frac{1}{6}l^3$). Since this can also be written as $\frac{1}{3}l^2 \times \frac{1}{2}l$ and thence as

$\frac{1}{3}$ × area of base × height, it serves as an illustration of the truth of the formula for similar square based pyramids. It is not a proof that the formula is true for other square based pyramids or any other pyramids. It is important for pupils to realise that a demonstration of truth for a particular case, or even a group of particular cases, is not equivalent to a generalised proof.

Approximate Proof

Unfortunately a proof that the volume of a pyramid is $\frac{1}{3}A \times h$ is beyond most fifteen and sixteen year old pupils. However the idea that the volume of a cone can be visualised as the sum of the volumes of infinitely many infinitesimally thin discs and then approximated as a tower of discs of unit thickness and decreasing radii, as shown below, may be accessible to some pupils.

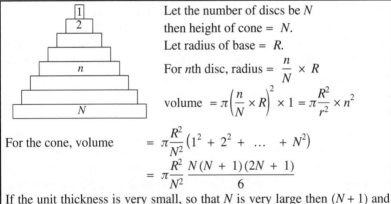

Let the number of discs be N

then height of cone = N.

Let radius of base = R.

For nth disc, radius = $\dfrac{n}{N} \times R$

volume $= \pi\left(\dfrac{n}{N} \times R\right)^2 \times 1 = \pi\dfrac{R^2}{r^2} \times n^2$

For the cone, volume $\quad = \pi\dfrac{R^2}{N^2}\left(1^2 + 2^2 + \ \ldots\ + N^2\right)$

$\quad = \pi\dfrac{R^2}{N^2}\ \dfrac{N(N + 1)(2N + 1)}{6}$

If the unit thickness is very small, so that N is very large then $(N + 1)$ and $(2N + 1)$ can be approximated by N and $2N$ respectively.

$\quad \therefore\ \text{Volume}\ \approx\ \dfrac{\pi R^2}{N^2} \times \dfrac{2N^3}{6}\ =\ \dfrac{\pi R^2}{3} \times N$

i.e. the volume of a cone $= \frac{1}{3}\pi r^2 h\ =\ \frac{1}{3}$ area of base × height.

Number

0·9̇ = 1?

The possibility of the equality of 0·9̇ and 1 was considered at a superficial level in Chapter 2. Pupils studying proof at Proof Level 5 could discuss critically the relative merits of the various justifications listed in "Are You Sure?" (1999, French and Stripp (Eds.), p 1), namely, a numerical argument, continuing the pattern, an algebraic argument, and summing a geometric series.

Although some very able pupils could read and understand the discussion about this in the commentary (p 73), and possibly also the recommended further reading (Burn, 1997) a class discussion would be preferable. The inconclusive nature of the commentary may be a spur for some pupils to begin reading mathematics with more interest.

Paradoxes

Achilles and the tortoise

This paradox is known as Zeno's second. The argument suggests that if Achilles gives the tortoise a head start, he can never overtake even though Achilles runs at 10 m/s and the tortoise travels at 1 m/s. For instance, if the tortoise had a start of 100 metres, then while Achilles was running this first 100 metres in one second the tortoise would have gone a further one metre. Achilles runs this distance in 1/10 second and the tortoise is still 1/10 metre ahead. The time taken for Achilles to catch up is given by the apparently infinite series 10 + 1 + 1/10 + 1/100 + 1/1000 + ..., suggesting that catching up is impossible! However its value is finite $(11\frac{1}{9})$ and the error induced by assuming time and distance are discrete is resolved.

2 is not prime

If 2 is prime it is the only even prime of infinitely many other primes. So the probability of an even number being prime is 1 divided by infinity which is zero. Thus it is impossible for any even number to be prime and therefore 2 is not prime. The error here is to fail to distinguish between infinitesimally small and zero. Whilst for practical purposes such a probability is zero, theoretically it is infinitesimally small and therefore the existence of 2 as an even prime is possible.

Assessment

During this phase the intention has been to enable pupils to perceive proof as an integral part of the mathematics curriculum, and not as a separate strand. It is therefore inappropriate to attempt to assess ability to prove independently of other mathematics. Instead proof should be assessed simultaneously with other aspects of the mathematics curriculum.

For instance, in geometry, in addition to calculations with reasons pupils could be required to use known and proven facts to produce abstract proofs of further properties. Some traditional textbooks, e.g."Geometry for Schools" (Palmer and Parr, 1938), are a useful source of problems. The following four are selected from this text:–

i) Prove that if a parallelogram is inscribed in a circle, it must be a rectangle. (p 180, q. 19)

ii) An isosceles triangle ABC with $AB = AC$ is inscribed in a circle. BC is produced to D, and AD meets the circle again at E; EC is joined. Prove that angle CED is equal to angle ACB. (p 180, q 22)

iii) AB and AC are equal chords of a circle. BC is produced to D so that $CD = CA$. DA cuts the circle at E. Prove that BE bisects angle ABC. (p 183, q 20)

iv) P is the mid-point of an arc AB of a circle. Prove that AP bisects the angle between the chord AB and the tangent at A. (p 237, q 17)

Similarly, although full solutions to equations may be considered as proofs, additional problems are again provided by traditional texts, e.g. "A School Algebra" (Channon and McLeish Smith, 1948). The following three problems are from this source:–

i) Prove that half the sum of any four consecutive numbers is an odd number, and that the sum of their squares, diminished by 5, is the square of this odd number. (p 352, q 13)

ii) Find a number of two digits which exceeds four times the sum of its digits by 3, and which is increased by 18 when the digits are interchanged. (p 353, q 19)

iii) "The sum of the squares of any two numbers is equal to one half of the sum of the squares of their sum and their differences." Express this statement in algebraic form and prove that it is true. Hence, or otherwise, prove that $(x + 2y)^2 + (2x + y)^2 = \frac{9}{2}(x + y)^2 + \frac{1}{2}(x - y)^2$. (p 365, q 5)

Finally, on a more modern note, some current texts, e.g. "Revision and Practice" (Rayner, 1994) include suggestions for coursework which can be extended to include the requirement to prove conjectures whenever possible. Past papers of some non-coursework GCSE examinations provide a similar source of appropriate opportunities for proof, even if this is not stated as an explicit requirement.

Conclusion

Although the material in this chapter is only likely to be appropriate for a minority of pupils, depriving such pupils of exposure to proof will significantly impoverish their experience, and may impair their future development, in mathematics.

There are several constraints which might influence a decision about spending time on proof discussions and activities. Some classes are large and have a wide range of ability; even some top sets may span up to 30% of the ability range. However in the classes described in this chapter, ranging from twenty-three to thirty pupils, not only the most able pupils took part in discussions; all pupils were directly involved in the initial stages of proof activities and in writing reports.

Some teachers may consider that there is insufficient time to include proof, because of the demands of other components of the mathematics curriculum. However, proof is not intended as an additional component requiring extra time, but as a new dimension providing an alternative approach. While it may take longer to introduce a new topic through a proof discussion this generates a deeper understanding than pupils accepting a new mathematical property or process on trust, and so less time may be required for reinforcement. This certainly seemed to be true for the pupils in the experimental group whose performance in end-of-year examinations was not adversely affected by a programme of study which emphasised proof. Six pupils in the group (25%) later gained A grades in GCSE Mathematics and two of these went on to achieve B and C grades in A-level Mathematics.

Finally, there may be concern that, because many pupils currently have little prior experience of proof, its introduction at the latter stages of compulsory schooling may create adverse reactions in pupils. However interviews with four very able sixteen year old pupils, described in the next chapter, suggest the reverse to be the case. Three of them indicated obvious pleasure and satisfaction in the notion of proof. The fourth, initially lacking confidence in her own ability to prove, acknowledged its important rôle in mathematics. When pupils are introduced to the notion of proof at an earlier stage in their mathematical education this will cease to be a problem.

CHAPTER 5

Proof in sixth forms and colleges

Three types of students with little, or no, prior knowledge of mathematical proof are exposed to notions of proof. Those needing help with basic numeracy are intrigued by the reasons behind some elementary mathematics. A general course about proof for non-mathematicians is outlined, and activities involving proof are suggested for students at the beginning of an A-Level Mathematics course. Thus at the post-sixteen phase this chapter offers ideas about –

proof for all.

Introduction

Since it seems likely that for some years to come some pupils will enter sixth forms and colleges with little or no experience of proof, it would seem appropriate to consider how to introduce older students to the notion of proof. For those studying A-level mathematics it is strongly recommended that this should be effected early in their course so that they learn to appreciate that proof is an intrinsic part of mathematics. It may also be possible to offer students who have elected to study other subjects a course of proof in mathematics as part of a general studies course, at a level appropriate to their mathematical ability. It is also possible that some older students who lack skills in numeracy might benefit from a proof-based approach.

All these groups could benefit by exposure to some of the proof discussions and activities already suggested for younger pupils. Those aiming to improve levels of basic numeracy could usefully consider some of the elementary properties of number. Students studying A-level mathematics, and some following a general course, could be introduced to the idea that mathematics is an example of a logical system with proof at its core. Those studying A-level mathematics should be enabled, through discussion, to develop proofs for all the new ideas they are taught, although these are not discussed here. They should also be given opportunities to construct proofs for themselves.

This chapter includes suggestions about how some of the activities described in earlier chapters might be used with three types of sixth form groups, namely, those who still need support in becoming numerate, those pursuing non-mathematical academic courses, and those studying mathematics beyond GCSE. For the latter group there is also a useful selection of proofs in "Are You Sure?" by French and Stripp (1999). Although some of these have direct links with aspects of the A-level syllabus there are also proofs of surprising and more unusual results. The proofs are in a formal style as might be expected at this level but the explanatory notes are less formal and should help students understand both individual proofs and the notion of proof *per se*. Interspersed throughout the text there are also results for students to try to prove, with model proofs in the commentary at the end of the book.

At present many students in sixth forms and colleges are likely to have little or no prior experience of proof. In order to demonstrate how some pupils might react to the notion of proof when it is introduced at this stage, the next section describes some interviews with students. The first set of interviews with four very able sixteen year olds were part of the research into pupil reactions to proof. There are then brief references to two eighteen year old students at opposite ends of the spectrum of mathematical ability, and a mature student preparing for GCSE examinations.

Student reactions to proof

The two boys (Alan and Ben) and two girls (Alice and Beryl) interviewed had virtually no experience of proof before discussing the three tasks described in the previous chapter, and reprinted below. They were selected on the recommendation of their teachers as being capable of the highest grade at GCSE. Both boys, and Alice achieved gold awards in the National Mathematics Challenge and Beryl elected not to enter. Alan and Alice recognised and applied the patterns to solve all three given tasks almost on sight, without writing down or expressing orally, until prompted, how they did this. The other two pupils analysed the patterns in a similar way to the more capable pupils in the experimental group.

All four pupils reacted hesitantly to requests to explain the patterns. Even the most able initially responded by giving further applications, albeit with reference to these being "random examples". They were clearly not familiar with the notion of proof and were unsure how to react. Thus their initial Proof Levels were 0 to 2.

However once the first task had been discussed in this way the idea became more familiar and, although they did not always justify patterns spontaneously, they were able to construct a proof with little or no intervention. Although they had all initially assumed their patterns to be universally applicable, they readily accepted the need to justify their assumptions, and ultimately appeared to attain Proof Levels 4 or 5.

Task 1

Pupil Challenge

Squares of squares

'Squares of squares' are made with matches as shown in the diagram below:

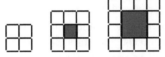

For example a 2 × 2 'square of squares' has 4 edge squares and uses 12 matches; and a 3 × 3 'square of squares' has 8 edge squares and uses 24 matches.

How many edge squares and how many matches will be needed to make a 25 × 25 'square of squares'?

Alan had recognised and used multiples of twelve and four from the given values and when he was asked whether he was justified in using these for the larger square his reaction indicated that he had not considered this. However, once he appreciated the need for an explanation he had no difficulty in relating the patterns to the structure of the problem. Recognising the pattern and explaining it took about three minutes.

Alice based her calculations for a 25 × 25 grid on an analysis of the structure of the diagrams. She perceived the number of matches as made up of left and right rows of matches for left and right rows of squares (25 × 4), top and bottom rows of matches for top and bottom rows of squares excluding corners (23 × 4), horizontal partitions for side squares (26 × 2) and vertical partitions across the top and bottom (22 × 4). When she was asked to generalise the results of her analysis of the structure of the diagrams she readily replaced 25 by n, simplified the resulting algebra, and explained how the simplified versions related to the diagrams.

After starting Task 1 by using the pattern of doubling, Beryl went on to recognise differences of four and then, after questioning, to see and use multiples of four. Later discussion revealed that these two ideas were equivalent in her mind and so she had not expressed the fact that the values were multiples of four. When asked whether she was justified in using the patterns for the larger square she hesitated, and then said, somewhat reluctantly, "I'd need to prove it." The reluctance was because she could not initially do this unaided, but needed very little intervention to construct a proof.

Ben used the diagram to find the number of edge squares by adding the top and bottom rows and then the sides, recognising there were two fewer to be counted in each side. (i.e. $25 + 25 + 23 + 23$). In an attempt to find the number of matches he first tried doubling and was satisfied with this until, after being asked how he could check this, he counted the 4×4 square. He noticed differences of four and twelve, and that he could find m by repeated addition but that this would be tedious. He then noticed and used the fact that $m = 3e$. In response to the question of universal validity he said, "I'm fairly sure it always works but I can't prove it." However he required little help in constructing the proof.

Task 2

> ## Pupil Challenge
>
> ### One less than square
>
> Look at this pattern:
>
> Line 1 $2^2 - 1 = 3 = 1 \times 3$
>
> Line 2 $3^2 - 1 = 8 = 2 \times 4$
>
> Line 3 $4^2 - 1 = 15 = 3 \times 5$
>
> Find, without using a calculator, the value of $999^2 - 1$.

Alan, Alice and Beryl recognised the pattern in Task 2 almost instantly as the product of $n - 1$ and $n + 1$, and Ben as "One more than n times two less than that."

Alan calculated $999^2 - 1$ almost immediately, then added the fourth line of the pattern to check that he had used it correctly. When asked repeatedly if this meant the pattern would always work, he first suggested he could check it for a few random numbers, and then that he could check $999^2 - 1$ on a calculator, but had no further suggestions. However when prompted by the question as to how he could represent any square number responded immediately by drawing 2×2 and 3×3 square grids with a unit square removed from the corner. He needed very little additional help in order to explain the structure of the problem for these cases and to extend this to a 999×999 square, and then to an $n \times n$ square.

Alice also recognised the patterns and used them to solve the problem almost instantly and her response to the question of universal validity of the pattern was "It seems all right so far!" When asked to provide a convincing argument wrote out the next four lines of the pattern. However when the difficulty of testing for all values was raised she appreciated the need for a general argument and did not hesitate to use algebra to write down and explain a general statement. When asked if she could think of a non-algebraic explanation replied negatively. However the diagrammatic approach was suggested after discussion of Task 3, and she took an active part in its use, but did not prefer this approach to the algebraic proof. She said that she had thought of squares but it had not occurred to her that it might be relevant.

Beryl said that she was not really justified in using the pattern for $999^2 - 1$ because she had not proved it, and added that she did not like proving. She needed several prompts to elicit the response that she could use algebra, which she did competently. In view of her feelings about proving, the possibility of a different approach was not suggested.

In response to the question of universal validity, Ben said that he could test for several values but realised the limitation of this, and then used algebra to construct a proof. When questioned about an alternative approach he did not spontaneously think of drawing a diagram but was able to follow this proof.

Task 3

Pupil Challenge

Reverse and subtract

In the following subtractions the second number has been formed by reversing the digits of the first:

$$73 - 73 = \qquad 52 - 25 = \qquad 60 - 06 =$$

Find the answers to these subtractions.

Use connections between the results to find $94 - 49$ without subtraction!

In Task 3 Ben recognised multiples of nine instantly, Alan and Alice realised this after examining factors of the results, and Beryl needed to do more examples before recognising multiples of three and then of nine. They all noticed the connection with the difference between the digits with very little or no intervention.

When Alan was asked if the pattern he had used would always work he pondered for some time without coming to any conclusion, and so was asked if he thought there was a reason. The fact that he began to write his ideas down suggested that he did, but in fact he was checking that the pattern worked "in reverse," by examining $37 - 73$, and was satisfied that it did. When the question of universal validity was again posed he attempted an algebraic approach, clearly appreciating that an explanation existed. He initially wrote $xy - yx$ and immediately realised that this was wrong but was unable to correct it. He then considered some more cases, used the vertical layout for subtraction (without prompting), but as he could not see how this could help, used a branching search and decided to investigate addition instead. He had no difficulty in finding and explaining why the results were multiples of eleven but could not relate this directly to the problem of subtraction. He was able to consider 73 as $70 + 3$ when this was suggested, and this led to the consideration of 36 as $40 - 4$. However, he was still unable to explain why the result was a multiple of 9 and so was encouraged to look at other cases and this eventually led to an understanding of the structure of the problem. He was then reminded of his earlier attempt to use algebra and asked if he could improve on it. He almost immediately began a correct algebraic proof based on simplifying and factorising $(10a + b) - (10b + a)$ and was obviously satisfied on its completion.

Alice took a little longer to recognise the patterns, hesitated slightly when asked if she were justified in using them to solve the problem, but then launched confidently into the algebraic proof described above. Informal discussion with her after solving the problems indicated that she was "not used to this sort of work" and was under the impression that her teacher thought her methods were "bizarre." Although she had confused proof and demonstration during the interview she clearly understood the general nature of each proof. She did not seem to have had an initial awareness of the need for proof but once this was pointed out to her she had no difficulty in transferring this realisation to later problems or in constructing her own proofs.

Ben thought that the results were not a coincidence but was unable to offer an explanation. He understood the numerical argument when this was discussed but was not persuaded that it constituted a proof and was clearly looking for a general argument. The possibility of an algebraic approach with two-digit numbers represented by ab and ba was suggested and he said he had thought of this earlier and realised it was wrong. With very little guidance he was able to construct a correct algebraic proof which he clearly found satisfying, saying, "I like this proof much better then the first one."

Beryl was asked whether she thought the pattern would always work. She replied, "I would hope it always works but that means I've got to prove it!" The possibility of using $ab - ba$ was raised, discussed and corrected by her to give $(10a + b)(10b + a)$ and complete the proof. She found this satisfying and replied, "I'm getting there!" She seemed to be admitting a reluctant acknowledgement of the importance of proof in mathematics, despite her own lack of confidence in constructing proofs.

The reactions of these pupils to the notion of proof can be summarised as follows: Alan already sensed the nature and necessity of proof and was able to construct proofs; Alice and Ben were willing converts to the power of proof and this awakened a realisation of the need for proof, which they could combine with their analytical ability to enable them to construct proofs; Beryl, while willing to accept the power of proof, was more reluctant to admit to its necessity due to lack of confidence in her ability to construct a proof. For Alice and Alan their newly acquired appreciation of proof combined with their competence in creating proofs of all three problems, almost independently, suggests that they are at Proof Level 5. The degree of help needed by Ben and Beryl suggests that Proof Level 4 is more appropriate. Once the question of proof was raised in the minds of these pupils they were quick to perceive its power and in many cases able to construct their own proofs. There were also expressions of pleasure and satisfaction on completion of some proofs.

Three informal contacts with older learners illustrate very different, but positive, reactions to proof. A conversation with an exceptionally able sixth former (not taught mathematics by the author), who was later to read mathematics at Cambridge, revealed that, although he was not always expected to prove new A-level mathematics, he clearly felt the need to do this and had created his own proofs and published them on the Internet.

A second eighteen year old who struggled with basic numeracy was initially bemused. He then seemed to enjoy, questioning half-remembered rules like Area of a rectangle = length × width. Informal discussion with a mature (aged 40+ years) student after an individual tutorial, based on the same material and also elementary properties of angles, indicated that the approach was found interesting because it was novel, and helpful in that it considered patterns and relationships in mathematics not previously recognised. According to this lady the tutorial had "revealed ideas that had previously lain dormant."

A proof-based approach to elementary mathematics

Clearly such anecdotal evidence as that described above must be viewed with caution, but it is at least possible that a change of approach to mathematics may at least benefit other older learners of similar ability. The novelty of gaining a sense that there is an underlying logic to mathematics that allows all its premises to be questioned once a few basic axioms are agreed could be motivating for some students.

All of the Proof Discussions from Phase 1 and most from Phase 2 could be appropriate in these circumstances. Discussion of the number properties can usefully be preceded by brief reference to the history of the development of number leading to the importance of ten, which could loosely be described as a basic axiom of number at this level. It is unlikely that using algebra at this stage would be helpful in the discussions of number properties. The formulae for calculating areas and volumes should be preceded by discussion to establish precisely what each is and how they are measured. A second axiom in this context is the definition of π as the ratio of the circumference and radius of a circle. If elementary geometry is to be included the basic angle properties can all be deduced from only two further axioms: that angles at a point sum to $360°$ and parallel lines are in the same direction as each other.

Although the Proof Activities are likely to be less relevant for older learners, consideration of the activities "Reverse and add" and "Reverse and subtract" provides practice in the mechanics of two-digit addition and subtraction enhanced by an opportunity to deepen understanding. In a one-to-one or small group context it may be possible to go on to consider three digit numbers using generic examples in preference to algebraic explanations.

Proof for general sixth form courses

Although competence in mathematics to at least Grade C in GCSE is preferred, this is not essential as there is little reference to use of algebra as this is an area of mathematics that many non-mathematicians find difficult. The emphasis is to introduce mathematics as an example of a logical system. It is still preferable at this stage if all the properties considered are discussed with the students but it is not impossible to base a lecture course around the same material. For both purposes the following outline, containing proofs from all three Proof Phases, is suggested.

Number

Combining odd and even numbers

Most students will be aware of these properties and have an intuitive understanding about why the results occur. However they may experience difficulty in explaining this concisely and precisely. They will therefore appreciate the "Picture Proofs" (pp 24,29 and 90) and some may benefit from also considering the algebraic alternative.

Adding consecutive numbers

Some students in a non-mathematical sixth form group are likely to be among those who fail to recognise the sequence 1, 4, 9, 16, ... as square numbers. They might see differences of odd numbers. They are likely to appreciate the diagrammatic proof of the connection (p 30). They could also be shown the diagrammatic representation of the *n*th triangle number as the sum of the first *n* integers (pp 30 and 126) and the formation of square numbers from the sum of two consecutive triangle numbers (p 31). Taken together these connections emphasise the unity of mathematics. If the course being studied includes individual assignments students might be asked to analyse a problem involving triangle numbers, such as "Handshakes" (p 71) or "Crossing Lines" (p 127). Finally, if time permits, this section might also include adding different numbers of consecutive integers not necessarily including one, as in the activity "Staircase Numbers" (p 115).

Divisibility tests

Explanations of these could be preceded by a brief introduction to the history of number to include reference to the existence of bases other than ten (e.g.. in Imperial measures) and the fact that the base of ten for the current system can be perceived as an axiom of number. Whether or not an algebraic approach is used to explain the divisibility tests will depend on the ability and interest of the students. To further illustrate the decimal nature of the current number system, and to provide a context for using the divisibility test for nine, the activities "Reverse and Add" (p 63) and "Reverse and Subtract" (p 69) might be suggested to interested students.

Product of three consecutive integers

Students are unlikely to be aware that the result of multiplying three consecutive integers is always a multiple of six (pp 149–151). It is probably not worth spending a long time discovering this result but its proof is well worth discussing. The fact that it is more easily explained without algebra than with algebra is likely to appeal to non-mathematicians.

Commutativity

The simplest examples of commutativity are addition and multiplication of numbers as described in Phase 1 (p 34), but other examples of commutative operations could be used.

Fermat numbers

The proof element here, that of the inadvisability of forming conclusions without proof and a proof by counter-example (p 167), is enhanced by the fact that large numbers themselves have an appeal which is enhanced by an awareness of their use in encoding confidential information. If time permits and the students are sufficiently motivated it may be possible to organise a debate about the issue of acceptability of a computer proof.

Mensuration

Area of rectilinear figures

Students are likely to react in a similar way to the fourteen and fifteen year old pupils described earlier (p 92) to the notion that even basic formulae, like that for the area of a rectangle, can be logically explained. Although students are reasonably likely to have met the deductive proofs for the remaining rectilinear figures the proofs should be mentioned to highlight the existence of a logical basis for them all, and to point out that, except for agreed axioms, there is nothing in mathematics which cannot be subjected to proof. It may be appropriate to challenge the students to think of something in mathematics that cannot be proved!

Circumference and area of circles

The first formula associated with circles ($C = 2\pi r$) is based on a definition which can be used as an example of an axiom. Again, something of the history of the number π is likely to be of interest. It is still not possible to use calculus to prove the formula for the area of a circle but a deeper understanding of this can be achieved by using this context to raise awareness of the concept of infinity. The method of forming an approximate circle from a spiral of string, as described on page 95 can be used as an alternative to the more familiar dissections.

Volumes

The formulae for the volumes of cuboids and other prisms can be deduced as those for areas above, but since the arguments are very similar it may be decided to omit these. It is however worthwhile to consider the formula for the volume of a pyramid. This context can be used to highlight the difference between assumptions based on empirical evidence (p 210), a demonstration for a particular case (p 219), and the existence of a deductive proof, although it may be considered that the example given on page 211 is too difficult for some students.

Geometry

Although students are likely to be familiar with much of the content of this section they are less likely to have been exposed to the perspectives adopted here.

Angles

The basic angle properties provide a simple example of a series of logical deductions from two basic axioms, as described on pages 35–41. The various proofs about angles in triangles provide an example of proving something in different, but equally valid, ways.

Pythagoras' theorem

It is possible that some students may have been shown Perigal's dissection as a proof of Pythagoras' theorem. Whether or not this is the case the fact that it may involve a false deduction can be highlighted by reference to the "Square dissection" on page 160. The result of Pythagoras' theorem can also be used as an example of a mathematical property which can be proved in several different ways. Those quoted on pages 180 and 181 can be considered and/or students asked to find their own proofs for consideration in a later session.

Circle theorems

Students are likely to have been introduced to the properties associated with angles in and tangents to circles, but currently they are unlikely to have proved these. It is worth emphasising to students that the primary interest here is not mastery of geometrical calculations, but how the properties are proved and use of formal mathematical language. This introduction to Euclidean geometry, albeit somewhat superficial, can also be justified on the grounds that Euclidean geometry is arguably an important part of western mathematical culture.

The first theorem about angles at the centre and circumference of a circle is a straightforward deduction based on elementary geometry (angles in triangles) which can be presented in the standard verbal-algebraic form and/or diagrammatically (p 174). The second approach, which is likely to be unfamiliar, also introduces the use of the symbol for "because". Brief consideration of the properties which follow from this first theorem provides an opportunity to explain the meaning of a corollary.

Most students readily accept that a vertical diameter of a circle standing on a horizontal tangent intersects the point of contact. This acceptance provides a useful opportunity to distinguish between proof and conjecture. It may be appropriate at this point to introduce the activity about "Regions in a circle" (p 157) to further emphasise the danger of accepting as fact that which has not been subjected to proof.

The proof of the mutual perpendicularity of radius and tangent is by contradiction (p 176) which is likely to be an unfamiliar style of logical argument, but accessible to able students. If the Alternate Segment Theorem and the equality of tangents from a point are included the proof of the latter should not use the conditions for congruent triangles unless these are first explained, possibly along the lines described on pages 96–99.

Euler's Theorem

In addition to an unusual proof (p 197), which involves the transformation of a three dimensional problem into one of two dimensions and has both inductive and deductive components, the context of solid shapes provides experience in thinking in three dimensions and the opportunity to enhance the mathematical vocabulary of students by naming the shapes.

Fallacies and paradoxes

Puzzles like fallacies and paradoxes appeal to many people and serve here as examples of inconclusive and erroneous arguments. The simple, well-known paradoxes "True or false?" (p 84) and "Achilles and the tortoise" (p 212) are worth including. Zeno's first paradox argues that motion is impossible and is described in many books of puzzles and diversions in mathematics (e.g. Northrop, p 118). The fallacies, quoted on page ??, that purport to prove "2 = 1" and "−1 = 1" involve some use of algebra but they may be accessible to some students. Two simpler fallacies can be obtained by misapplying the basic axioms that the sum and product of "equals" are "equal". They are:

	1 cat has 4 legs		2 pounds = 32 ounces
	no (0) cat has 3 legs		½ pound = 8 ounces
(adding)	1 cat has 7 legs	(multiplying)	1 pound = 256 ounces

(Northrop, p 81)

Introduction to proof for A-level mathematics courses

Students who have been exposed to proof during the pre-A-Level phase will expect to construct or be shown proofs of all the mathematics they learn during A-level. However in the short and medium term this is an over-optimistic expectation. A-level students are more likely to react with surprise, but positive interest, when they first encounter the notion of proof. Although the material used in this course is similar to that in the "general" course, the approach is different. This is mainly due to the increased use of algebra, since it is assumed that the students are sufficiently competent in their use of algebra to create proofs independently or in discussions. A significant number in any group will respond positively to assignments in which they are invited to read about mathematics, and do independent investigations in preparation for some discussions.

The aim of this section is to raise student awareness of proof and to introduce several proof methods through some of the elementary properties previously described. Most of this work should be undertaken at the beginning of an A-level course so that the remainder of the mathematics learned may be linked, by a logical argument, to mathematics already known, thus presenting mathematics as an inter-connected logical system. Although in some syllabuses some results are quoted and used without proof there is a strong case for widening the scope of mathematics taught to include additional material to provide the necessary links. For instance it is unsatisfactory to teach pupils how to differentiate trigonometric functions without first considering the ratios for small angles.

There is no attempt in this book to discuss in detail the content of A-level mathematics, since its aim is limited to creating an approach to learning mathematics which expects explanations of all claims.

Number and algebra

The following pupil worksheet, which includes a number of activities suggested for younger pupils, has been used with students at the beginning of their A-level course. The students have been asked to work on the problems independently before the results have been discussed in class.

Proving facts about numbers

Give a numerical example of, and then use algebra to explain, the following:–

1. If a number is divisible by 9 then the sum of its digits is also divisible by 9.
2. The product of any three consecutive integers is divisible by 6.
3. If a number with an even number of digits is added to its "reverse" (e.g. 73 and 37) the result is a multiple of 11.
4. The difference between any number and its "reverse" is a multiple of 9.
5. If you find the product of any four consecutive positive integers and divide by 8 the result is a triangle number.
6. Given fifteen terms of a Fibonacci-like sequence, the sum of the first thirteen of them is equal to the fifteenth term minus the second term.

---

7. The sum of any ten consecutive terms in a Fibonacci-like
    sequence is eleven times the seventh term of the ten term
    sequence.

8. If two 2-digit numbers have the same tens digit, and units digits
    whose sum is ten, their product can be computed instantly.

9. If you multiply any four consecutive integers and add 1, the
    result is always a perfect square.

10. The sum of two consecutive triangle numbers is always a
    square number.

Note:– You may need to look up some of the terms used above.

The conjecture about Fermat numbers, and the proof that $\sqrt{2}$ is
irrational can be considered if time permits. Students could research
these themselves in preparation for a brief class discussion.

Pascal's triangle

This is "discovered" in two apparently different ways and an
attempt made to appreciate why this happens. This additional activity
is included as it could provide an informal introduction to a more
formal treatment of binomial expansion and combinations in addition
to Pascal's triangle. Prior knowledge of Pascal's triangle and
combinations is not assumed and it is preferable if students work
from first principles.

Students should investigate, in either order, the number of routes
to all intersections across a grid and the coefficients of binomial
expansions. Both of these produce the same set of numbers, i.e.
Pascal' triangle. The reason for this is unlikely to be appreciated by
students, unless they have previously studied combinations. Analysis
through class discussion will consider the number of ways of
selecting horizontal and vertical moves across the grid, and of
selecting, say x, in the binomial expansion of $(x + y)^n$, and so explain
the similarity of these.

Special arrangements

This activity is based on an article by Anderson and Austen
(1995), and described on pages 200 to 202. It can be used as a
starting point for a more complex investigation about arranging
larger sets of numbers. After the numbers of arrangements for four,
five, six and seven numbers have been found by logical reasoning,
the problem is reviewed and an attempt made to analyse the general

case. Reviewing the problem involves tabulating the results as shown below and forming a conjecture.

Number in set (n)	2	3	4	5	6	7
Number of solutions	2	2	4	4	8	8

At this stage, such a conjecture is unproved. The original problem, posed and analysed in concrete terms, now becomes analysis of the general case to prove that:–

the number of permutations of [1, 2, ..., n] in which adjacent terms sum to $n + 1$ is $2^{[n/2]}$, where [t] is the largest symbol not exceeding t.

Previous examination of left-to-right arrangements for small sets indicate that any solution must begin 1 n ~ ~ ...., leaving the problem of arranging the remaining ($n - 2$) numbers 2, 3, ..., $n - 1$ with adjacent pairs summing to at least $n + 1$. Reducing each number in this last set by one changes the problem to that of arranging 1, 2, ..., $n - 2$ so that adjacent pairs sum to at least $n - 1$, which is essentially the same as the general case. Each of these arrangements produces two arrangements for the original n numbers thus: 1, n, (arrangement of $n - 2$ numbers) and (arrangement of $n - 2$ numbers), n, 1.

The formal version of this proof by induction first checks the results for two and three numbers, assumes the result true for $n = k$, and then considers arrangements for $k = n - 2$ (or $n = k + 2$). Reference to the original article "Paradigms of Proof" in The Mathematical Gazette (Anderson and Austin, 1995), of which this is a brief summary, is strongly recommended. An alternative is to ask students to read the article themselves.

Mensuration

In previous phases the formula for finding the area of a rectangle, from which other formulae were deduced, was only justified by a partial proof (p 92). When students understand integral calculus the complete proof is accessible and the connections with other formula discussed briefly. Since finding the area of a circle by integration involves more difficult integration this may not be taught until later in the course. Instead the relative merits of the proofs by dissection and coiled string could be discussed as a concrete example of the abstract notion of tending to a limit. In this instance, as the size of a sector or the thickness of the string approaches zero, the area of the circle approaches πr^2.

Volumes of revolution are not generally introduced near the beginning of an A-level course and thus a complete proof for the volume of a pyramid is not accessible until later. Just before such a proof it is useful to review previous approaches, as discussed on pages 210–211. These can be contrasted with the complete proof of, say, the formula for the volume of a cone formed by rotating a straight line about an axis.

Geometry

Since proof in geometry has virtually disappeared in secondary schools any approach to this in the sixth form will need to begin at the beginning. A useful starting point is the comparison of proofs about angles in triangles along the lines described on pages 171–173. In the opinion of the writer there is a strong case to be made for exposing able students to some Euclidean geometry, partly so that future mathematicians should not be ignorant of this. If this is not done before A-level then sixth form students should at least be exposed to the circle theorems (pp 173–178), as examples of Euclidean geometry. These have the advantage of introducing a formal style of proof, and also some of the language associated with proof, e.g. corollary and converse.

There is also a case to be made on both historical and mathematical grounds for discussing with students the existence of many proofs for Pythagoras' theorem. After conceding that Perigal's dissection is not proof (possibly by reference to "Dissected square" on page 160) students could find one proof to present to the rest of the class for a later lesson. Corollaries could then be considered. These might include areas of semi-circles drawn on the sides of right-angled triangles, and the converse of Pythagoras' theorem and its corollary which provides tests to establish whether a triangle is acute or obtuse angled.

Finally, the activity "Regions in a circle" (p 157) is useful. Even for sixth form mathematics students it is an excellent illustration of the danger of accepting a conjecture without proof. As in the previous section this could be introduced with circle theorems, and contrasted with the fact that the propositions made about angles and tangents are all proved. An attempt could then be made to at least outline a proof, such as those published in three articles in

"Mathematics in Schools" (Beevers, 1994, Gardiner, 1995, and Anderson, 1995). Indeed, students could be asked to read an article and present either an oral or written summary.

Fallacies and paradoxes

Some of the fallacies and paradoxes described in earlier chapters could be researched by students independently and those that interest them shared with their peers in class discussion. The teacher can assist if necessary! Alternatively, if lack of time prevents this approach, the algebraic fallacies (p 159) can be used as examples to highlight common errors in algebra. Zeno's second paradox can be used as an interesting example of a geometric progression. The more general paradoxes and fallacies might be used when it is necessary to reinforce the distinction between proof and conjecture, or between a valid proof and a false proof.

Conclusion

This chapter has suggested three different ways in which mathematical proof might be of benefit to students in sixth forms and colleges.

The use of proof to introduce elementary number and geometry properties to older students seemed to have advantages, but these are only tentatively claimed, as more evidence is necessary before such an approach is formally recommended.

While able non-mathematical students might resist being introduced to new mathematics, in which they have little interest and for which they see little use, they might value the approach outlined above because the emphasis has moved away from teaching mathematical facts and towards the development of mathematical ideas through logical reasoning, in some cases set in an historical context. It also has the advantage that it fosters mathematical literacy, which supersedes numeracy.

It may seem that the approach for A-level mathematics necessarily involves teaching much additional material and that pressure of time precludes the possibility of this. However this need not be the case as many of the above discussions may be short and can be embedded in lessons involving other aspects of mathematics. For instance the "Proving Facts about Numbers" worksheet sets proof alongside the context of practising algebra, and the informal approaches to Pascal's triangle and area of a circle are short preludes to more formal mathematics in the A-level course. Some of the suggestions deliberately involve students in independent study to encourage them to take more responsibility for what they learn, which many teachers will agree is advisable, especially during the early phase of any A-level course.

CHAPTER 6

Implementing a proof-orientated curriculum

This last chapter re-emphasises the importance of providing proof opportunities in mathematics for pupils in school, and reviews the main recommendations in the teaching programme described in earlier chapters. It then considers how these might be implemented in the light of recent changes to the English National Curriculum for Mathematics. In highlighting the possibilities for teaching proof, and offering guidance to teachers leading class activities and discussions to create proofs, it is hoped this book achieves its primary intention of –

raising the profile of Proof in school mathematics.

The importance of proof

Many educators would agree that the following are amongst the most important reasons for teaching mathematics:–

- it creates an awareness of an important, and potentially exciting, area of development in human experience;
- its concepts and processes form a bank of knowledge to serve as tools for later life;
- it can provide learners with experience in logical thinking of particular kinds.

Most teachers pay some attention to the first two of these but the third is currently often forgotten. In the recent debate about the status of proof in the school mathematics curriculum most contributors regretted the almost total demise of proof from mathematics classrooms. Gardiner (1993, 1995a, and 1995b) wrote several articles justifying the inclusion of proof at this level, and claimed in one (1993, p 21) that "reasoning is more than a convenient mnemonic: it is the heart of the discipline (mathematics)". The author strongly supports this claim. Those teachers who, like the author, wish to maintain a balance between "mathematics as a form of thinking and reasoning" and the "content of mathematics" (Resnick and Ford, 1984, p 7) will be concerned that the last reason in the above list should not be neglected.

Although proof was never a significant part of the mathematics taught to most English pupils, it used to be included in the curriculum for able pupils. However, for more than twenty years scant attention has been paid to any type of proof by textbook and curriculum writers, and examination boards. Consequently many teachers have not thought it relevant for their pupils. Indeed some younger teachers may never have experienced it at school level. It is hoped that the information in this book might remedy the situation by raising the awareness of pupils, teachers, and others with control over what pupils learn, to the importance of proof in school mathematics.

The first chapter argued the case for raising the profile of proof in school mathematics, and described the development of pupils' perception and understanding of proof in six Proof Levels. It then outlined a teaching programme for introducing proof into mathematics classrooms. Subsequent chapters included guidance for leading proof discussions about a wide variety of mathematical concepts, and for extending investigations to create additional opportunities for proof. Teachers who read the introductory chapter learn of the importance of proof at school level. Those teachers who read chapters relevant to their level of teaching will find ideas and strategies for introducing proof to their pupils. Initially this is done with the emphasis on explaining patterns, but gradually pupils are introduced to other forms of proof.

A research teaching programme, which mainly used the domain of pattern, was successful in that the pupils in the experimental group learned to appreciate the notion of proof, and most could eventually prove in contexts involving visual patterns which led to number patterns. The emphasis, for these pupils, on explaining patterns and providing practice in recognising them, seemed to be at least as effective as the direct instruction in pattern-spotting techniques which had been given to pupils in one of the control groups. There was some concern that emphasising proof and pattern might adversely affect general mathematical attainment, due to consequent reduction in emphasis on practice. This does not seem to have happened.

The results of written tests and interviews indicated that appreciation of the need for, and nature of, proof and ability to create proofs were all enhanced by the research teaching programme. This suggests that teaching proof, in its broadest interpretation, is a viable proposition for older pupils in secondary schools.   The author's classroom experience indicates that younger pupils in secondary schools also benefit by being exposed to proof, especially proof based on pattern. There is also evidence that some primary school pupils have produced simple proofs indicating they understand the notion of proof (Jones, 1994 and Perks and Prestage, 1995).

Thus, on balance, the research showed that teaching proof through pattern made it accessible to pupils and gave some of them obvious satisfaction. Although their ability to prove was limited, this was an advance on total ignorance of proof, and was not at the expense of progress in other areas of mathematics. More recent classroom experience with other similar pupils has shown positive reactions to the ideas of proof by many pupils, followed by very pleasing examination performances by most. In addition to offering suggestions for proof activities based on pattern, this book has attempted to blend ideas of proof with other aspects of the mathematics curriculum.

A model for teaching proof

Three important suggestions about teaching proof, highlighted in the literature, are that it should be taught in context rather than isolation (Slomson, 1996), involve as wide a variety of proof methods as possible (Anderson and Austin, 1995, and be taught informally, through discussion (Neubrand, 1989). All three of these suggestions are incorporated into the model for teaching proof used in this book. The three phases in which it is taught reflect the intellectual development of pupils. In the first phase younger pupils and older beginners learn about proof, mainly in the context of explaining patterns. As they become more fluent in writing and logical thinking many pupils then progress to writing proofs as explanations of patterns. Some able pupils progress to the third phase during which they improve their proof skills to the level of beginning to read and write more formal proofs.

Although the domain of pattern has been shown to be appropriate, it is also advisable not to neglect to prove, or at least provide informal justification of, new mathematical ideas. This latter not only has the advantage of widening the variety of proof methods, but may also foster an approach to mathematics welcomed by some university teachers (e.g. Barnard and Saunders, 1994) and others (e.g. Jeffrey, 1977, and Skemp. 1971). The findings of the research indicated that able pupils can follow some Euclidean geometry proofs and therefore these should not be neglected for these pupils, even though they may not be appropriate for all. Where they are not appropriate it may be possible to use methods based on "intuitive conviction" (Fischbein, 1982) or "transformational reasoning" (Simon, 1996). These approaches avoid one of the major stumbling blocks for pupils: the use of formal language. Provided such proofs are introduced sensitively, and there is no element of rote learning, they could be useful ways of broadening pupils' proof experience.

However for most pupils they should not be over-emphasised. The domain of pattern is more motivating for most pupils and the relationships to be proved are not "obvious" to pupils, as are some geometry propositions. Within pattern it is possible to include a variety of proof types such as "action proofs" (Semadeni, 1984) and proofs with diagrams; and also proof methods such as proof by induction or deduction, and proof by counter-example. It is recognised that although this approach might widen access to proof to more pupils it is unlikely to be accessible to all. In using and adapting the material in this book for their own circumstances teachers will make their own judgements about the needs of their pupils, but the following guidelines might be helpful.

Many pupils could be introduced to proof at the level discussed in Chapter 2 in primary school. Most should then at least complete working at this level before the end of secondary schooling, and many pupils will benefit by some of the proof experiences described in Chapter 3. All mathematically able pupils, and especially those who might continue mathematical studies beyond the age of sixteen, are entitled to proof wherever possible, and informal explanations otherwise, of all the mathematics they are expected to learn, and at least an introduction to the more formal aspects of proof indicated by some of the discussions and activities suggested in Chapter 4. They should also be given opportunities to create proofs, and encouraged to develop a more formal style. If this is achieved before such pupils enter sixth forms then there will no longer be any need for most of the suggestions in Chapter 5.

Implementing the model

In an ideal world all pupils would be taught mathematics (and other subjects) by a specialist teacher able to tailor the mathematics taught to each individual child, and always be available to stimulate the child's mathematical thinking and respond to all questions. In such a situation each pupil would be provided with explanations, at a time and in such a way as to maximise their development in understanding mathematics, and coincidentally learn from the beginning that proof is an intrinsic part of mathematics. The revised English National Curriculum would seem to agree with the value of the early introduction of ideas of proof by making explicit reference at Key Stage 1 (p 39) to preparing pupils for proof at later key stages.

Although this approach is very warmly welcomed, the management of the introduction of this change of approach will need to take into account the fact that the neglect of proof has created a generation of teachers, in both primary and secondary schools, with minimal experience of proof in the classroom. Not only will these teachers need to be made aware of the important rôle of proof in school mathematics, but they will also need practical support in developing teaching strategies for introducing ideas of proof. This book includes examples of how proof can be used to explain familiar, and introduce new, topics in mathematics and thus create links within the subject. It is hoped that these examples will help teachers as they adapt to a proof-orientated approach to teaching mathematics.

In order to avoid some of the mistakes of the past, it is necessary to consider assessment of pupils' ability to prove. First, there is little value in pupils rote learning proofs and so there is little point in tests of this nature. Also, since proof is embedded in almost all other aspects of the mathematics curriculum it is neither wise nor necessary to isolate it for assessment in the school situation. Any test incorporating elements of proof will therefore necessarily involve other mathematical concepts.

Teachers will need to exercise caution in measuring pupils' ability to prove. They will realise that lack of written evidence of ability to prove does not necessarily mean that a pupil cannot prove. Other possible stumbling blocks to the creation of a proof may be difficulty in expressing a proof in writing, or difficulty with the mathematics forming the context of the proof. In reading pupils' proofs for assessment teachers will need to take care that not only are correct statements present, but also that they are in a logical order! Chapter 3 includes two suggestions for summative assessment of attainment in proof but, in the opinion of the author, these are far less valuable to pupils than formative assessment comprising helpful comments about their attempts at proof.

This book presents a strong case for increasing the emphasis on proof but this need not be done at the expense of other valuable mathematical activities. Without proof many pupils acquire mathematical competence by rote learning followed by practice exercises. Proof discussions and activities help pupils acquire a deeper understanding of mathematical concepts, and so less time is needed for routine practice. There is still a place for practice exercises but, as pupils are less dependent on these for learning new ideas, some time is released for proof. So it is not necessary to reduce the time spent on other mathematical activities in order to accommodate proof. Proof-orientated mathematics is an alternative approach to teaching mathematics. It is vitally important that proof should not be seen as an additional component requiring extra time.

Concluding comments

Education in any subject area is more likely to be effective if it capitalises on natural instincts and interests of learners. Mathematics which is proof-orientated provides a neutral domain in which pupils' inquisitiveness and developing ability to reason logically may both be exercised. Such an approach is likely to enhance pupils' understanding of other concepts in mathematics. Even though the pupils in the research acquired only limited skills in proving, their awareness of the need for, and nature of proof was raised. Although ability to prove may be constrained by context, it is arguably preferable, for pupils to prove in a restricted range of contexts than not to experience proof at all.

The final hope is that, in becoming mathematically literate, pupils end their period of compulsory education with some appreciation of the "wholeness" of mathematics, some pleasurable feelings at having made sense of at least some of what they learned, and an attitude of mind which causes them to ask questions and find reasons.

Bibliography

Anderson, J. (1995) "Patterns which aren't are!" *Mathematics in School*, **24,** (2), 20-22

Anderson, J. (1996) "The place of proof in school mathematics" *Mathematics Teaching*, (**155**), 33-39

Anderson, J. and Austin, K. (1995) "Paradigms of proof" *The Mathematical Gazette*, **79**, (486), 489-495

Balacheff, N. (1988) "Aspects of proof in pupils' practice of school mathematics" translated by Pimm, D in Pimm, D. (Ed.) *Mathematics, Teachers and Children* pp 216-235, The Open University

Ball, B. (1996) "How do I teach proof?" *Mathematics Teaching*, (**155**), 31-33

Ball, W. W. R. (1956) *Mathematical Recreations and Essays* McMillan

Barnard, A. and Saunders, P. (1994) "Superior sums that don't add up to much" in *The Guardian* (December 28th)

Beard, R.M. (1969) *An Outline of Piaget's Developmental Psychology* Routledge and Kegan Paul

Beevers, B. (1994) "Patterns which aren't" *Mathematics in School*, **23,** (5), 10-12

Bell, A.W. (1976) *The Learning of General Mathematical Strategies* Ph.D. Thesis, Nottingham

Bell, A.W., Costello, J., and Kuchemann, D. (1983) *A Review of Research in Mathematical Education Part A - Research on Learning and Teaching* NFER-Nelson

Blum, W. and Kirsch, A. (1991) "Preformal Proving: Examples and Reflections" *Educational Studies in Mathematics*, **22,** (2), 183-203

Brown, L. (1995) "Coming to know" *Mathematics in School*, **24,** (3), 36-38

Burn, R. (1997) "A case of conflict" *The Mathematical Gazette* **81,** (490), 109-112

Channon J. B. and McLeish Smith A. (1959) *A School Algebra* Longman

Devlin K. (1998) *Mathematics: the New Golden Age* Penguin

Dowling, P. and Noss, R. (1990) *Mathematics versus the National Curriculum* Falmer Press

Dreyfus, T. et al (1990) "Advanced Mathematical Thinking" in Nescher, P. and Kilpatrick, J. (Eds.) *Mathematics and Cognition* pp 125-13 Cambridge University Press

Ennis, R. (1969) *Logic in Teaching* Prentice Hall

Fischbein, E. (1982) "Intuition and proof" *For the Learning of Mathematics*, **3,** (2), 9-24

Fischbein, E. and Kedem, I. (1982) "Proof and certitude in the development of mathematical thinking" in Vermandel, A. (Ed.) *Proceedings of the Sixth International Conference PME*, pp 128-131

French, D.W. and Stripp, C. (1999) *Are You Sure? Learning about Proof* The Mathematical Association

Gardiner, A. (1987) *"Mathematical Puzzling"* Oxford University Press

Gardiner, A. (1993) "Recurring themes in school mathematics - reasons and reasoning" *Mathematics in School*, **22,** (1), 20-21

Gardiner, A. (1995a) "Back to the future" *The Mathematical Gazette*, (**486**), 79, 526-532

Gardiner, A. (1995b) "The proof of the pudding is in the ......" *Mathematics in School*, **24,** (3), 10-11

Giles, G. (1984) *"Number Patterns 2 - Further Mappings"* DIME Pre-Algebra Project - University of Stirling. Tarquin Publications, Norfolk

Hemmings, R. and Tahta, D. (1995) *Images of Infinity* Leapfrogs Group (1984)/Tarquin (1992)

Hewitt, D. (1992) "Trainspotters' Paradise" *Mathematics Teaching*, (**140**), 6-8

Hewitt, D. (1996) "Towards Proof" *Mathematics Teaching*, (**155**), 27-33

Hoyles, C. and Healy, L. (1999) "Can they prove it?" *Mathematics in School*, **28,** (4), 10-11

Jeffrey. R. (1977) "Making and Testing Conjectures" *The West London Mathematics Centre Journal*, (**3**), 15

Jones, L. (1994) "Reasoning, logic and proof at Key Stage 2" *Mathematics in School*, **25,** (5), 6-8

Kerslake, D. (1994) "Pattern power" *Micromath*, 10, (1), 23-24

Lakatos, I. (1976) *Proofs and Refutations* Cambridge University Press

Lovell, K. (1978) "Concept development" in Wain, G.T. (Ed.) *Mathematical Education*, pp 96-109 Van Nostrand Reinhold Company

Maher, C.A. and Martino, A.M.(1996) "Young children invent methods of proof" in Steffe, L.P. and Nesher, P (Eds) *Theories of Mathematical Learning* Erlbaum

Martin, W.G. and Harel, G. (1989) "Proof frames of preservice elementary teachers" *Journal for Research in Mathematics Education* (**1**), 41-51

McFarland, H.S.N. (1971) *Psychological Theory and Educational Practice* Routledge and Kegan Paul

Mish, F. (Ed.) (1991) *Webster's Ninth new Collegiate Dictionary* Merriam-Webster Inc.

National Curriculum (England and Wales) (2000)

Nelsen, R. (1995) "Proof without words: exercises in visual thinking" Classroom Research Materials, Mathematical Association of America (reviewed by Abbot, S. in *Mathematical Gazette*, **78**, (484), 177-178)

Neubrand, M. (1989) "Remarks on the acceptance of proofs: the case of some recently tackled major theorems" *For the Learning of Mathematics*, **9**, (3), 2-6

Northrop, E. P. (1961) *Riddles in Mathematics* Penguin Books

Palmer, A. H. G. and Parr H. E. (1938) *Geometry for Schools* Bell

Perks, P. and Prestage, S. (1995) "Why don't they prove?" *Mathematics in School*, **24**, (3), 43-45

Polya, G. (1990) *How to Solve It* (Second edition) Penguin Books

Pope, S (1996) "On the nature of proof" *Mathematics Teaching*, (155), 22-23

Porteous, K. (1986) "Children's appreciation of the significance of proof" in *The Proceedings of the Tenth International Conference for the PME* pp 392-397

Porteous, K. (1994) "When a truth is seen to be necessary" *Mathematics in School*, **23**, (5), 2-5

Rayner, D. (1994) Revision and Practice Oxford University Press

Reid, D. (1996) "Teaching and the rôle of proof" *Mathematics Teaching*, (**155**), 23-26

Resnick, L.B. and Ford, W.W. (1984) *The Psychology of Mathematics for Instruction* Erlbaum

Robinson, G.E. (1964) *An investigation of junior high school students' spontaneous use of proof to justify mathematical generalisations* Ph.D. thesis, University of Wisconsin, Madison.

Semadeni, Z. (1984) "Action proofs in primary mathematics teaching and in teacher training" *For the Learning of Mathematics*, **4**, (1), 32-34

Simon, M.A. (1996) "Beyond inductive and deductive reasoning: the search for a sense of knowing" *Educational Studies in Mathematics*, **30,** 197-210

Singh, S. (1997) *Fermat's Last Theorem* Fourth Estate (London)

Skemp, R.R. (1971) *The Psychology of Learning Mathematics* Pelican

Slomson, A. (1996) "Mathematical proof and its rôle in the classroom" *Mathematics Teaching*, (**155**), 10-13

Tahan, M. (1994) *The Man Who Counted* translated by Clark, L. and Reid, A. Canongate Press (Edinburgh)

Tahta, R. (1996) "A pennyworth on proof" *Mathematics Teaching*, (**155**), 14

Threadgill-Sowder, J. (1985) "Individual differences in mathematical problem solving" in Silver, E. A. (Ed.) *Teaching and Learning Mathematical Problem Solving* (pp 331-344) Erlbaum

Vinner, S. (1983) "The notion of proof - some aspects of students' views at the senior high level" in *The Proceedings of the Tenth International Conference for the PME*, pp 289-294

Waring, S. (1997) *The teaching and learning of proof and pattern in the age range fourteen to sixteen years* Ed. D. thesis, University of Leeds

Waring, S., Orton, A. and Roper, T. (1999) "Proof and Pattern" in Orton, A. (Ed.) *Pattern in the Teaching and Learning of Mathematics* (pp 192-206) Cassell

Williams, G. (1978) *An investigation of senior high school students' understanding of proof* Ph.D. thesis, University of Alabama, Edmonton.

Index